The Dawn of the World

Recital of the Ancient Myths in
the Roundhouse at Night

The Dawn of the World

MYTHS AND WEIRD TALES TOLD BY THE
MEWAN INDIANS OF CALIFORNIA

COLLECTED AND EDITED BY
C. HART MERRIAM

CLEVELAND
The Arthur H. Clark Company
1910

Contents

PART 2: PRESENT DAY MYTHS

Contents

Illustrations

Illustrations

Preface

IT is our custom to go abroad for the early beliefs of mankind and to teach our children the mythologies of foreign lands, unmindful of the wealth and beauty of our American folk-tales. The present collection invites attention to the unique and entertaining character of the myths of some of our California Indians.

These tales were told me by the Indians of a single stock, the Mewan, the tribes of which are confined to central California and have no known relatives in any part of the world. They have been little visited by ethnologists and during the few years that have passed since the tales were collected, several of the tribes have become extinct.

The myths are related by the old people after the first rains of the winter season, usually in the ceremonial roundhouse and always at night by the dim light of a small flickering fire. They constitute the religious history of the tribe, and from time immemorial have been handed down by word of mouth; from generation to generation they have been repeated, without loss and without addition.

The conceptions of the Indians concerning the forces of nature and the character and attributes of the early inhabitants of the earth differ so radically

15

from our own that an explanation seems necessary. This is supplied by the Introduction, which is intended to give the reader the view point necessary for the full appreciation and enjoyment of the tales.

C. HART MERRIAM

Washington, D.C., January, 1910.

Introduction

THE mythology of the Indians of California goes back much farther than our mythology: it goes back to the time of the FIRST PEOPLE — curious beings who inhabited the country for a long period before man was created.

The myths of the Mewan tribes abound in magic, and many of them suggest a moral. They tell of the doings of the FIRST PEOPLE — of their search for fire; of their hunting exploits; of their adventures, including battles with giants and miraculous escapes from death; of their personal attributes, including selfishness and jealousy and their consequences; of the creation of Indian people by a divinity called Coyote-man; and finally of the transformation of the FIRST PEOPLE into animals and other objects of nature.

Some explain the origin of thunder, lightning, the rainbow, and other natural phenomena; some tell of a flood, when only the tops of the highest mountains broke the waves; others of a cheerless period of cold and darkness before the acquisition of the coveted heat and light-giving substance, which finally was stolen and brought home to the people.

2

FUNDAMENTAL ELEMENTS OF MEWAN MYTHOLOGY

The more important features of Mewan Mythology may be summarized as follows:

The existence of a FIRST PEOPLE, beings who differed materially from the present Indians, and who, immediately before the present Indians were created, were transformed into animals, trees, rocks, and in some cases into stars and other celestial bodies or forces — for even *Sah'-win-ne* the Hail, and *Nuk'-kah* the Rain were FIRST PEOPLE.

The preëxistence of Coyote-man, the Creator, a divinity of unknown origin and fabulous 'magic,' whose influence was always for good.[1]

The existence (in some cases preëxistence) of other divinities, notably *Wek'-wek* the Falcon, grandson and companion of Coyote-man, *Mol'-luk* the Condor, father of *Wek'-wek*, and *Pe-ta'-le* the Lizard, who, according to several tribes, assisted Coyote-man in the creation of Indian people.

The possession of supernatural powers or magic by Coyote-man, *Wek'-wek*, and others of the early divinities, enabling them to perform miracles.

The prevalence of universal darkness, which in the beginning overspread the world and continued for a very long period.

The existence at a great distance of a primordial heat and light giving substance indifferently called fire, sun, or morning — for in the early myths these were considered identical or at least interconvertible. [2]

The presence of a keeper or guardian of the fire, it being

---

[1] Partial exceptions, doubtless a result of contact with neighboring stocks, occur in two tribes: the *Wi'-pa* say that Coyote-man boasted beyond his powers; and the *Northern Mewuk* say that he was selfish.

[2] A partial exception is the belief of the Hoo-koo-e-ko of Tomales Bay who say that in the beginning the source of light was *He'-koo-las* the Sun-woman, whose body was covered with shining abalone shells.

foreseen by its first possessors that because of its priceless value efforts would be made to steal it.

The theft of fire, which in all cases was stolen from people or divinities living at a great distance.

The preservation of the stolen fire by implanting it in the *oo'-noo* or buckeye tree, where it was and still is, accessible to all.

The power of certain personages or divinities – as *Ke'-lok* the North Giant, *Sah'-te* the Weasel-man, and *O-wah'-to* the Bigheaded Lizard – to use fire as a weapon by sending it to pursue and overwhelm their enemies.

The conception of the sky as a dome-shaped canopy resting on the earth and perforated, on the sides corresponding to the cardinal points, with four holes which are continually opening and closing. A fifth hole, in the center of the sky, directly overhead, is spoken of by some tribes.

The existence, at or near the north hole in the sky, of Thunder Mountain, a place of excessive cold.

The presence of people on top of or beyond the sky.

The presence of people on the underside of the earth. (This belief may not be held by all the tribes.)

The existence of Rock Giants, who dwelt in caves and carried off and devoured people.

The tendency of the dead to rise and return to life on the third or fourth day after death.

The prevention of the rising of the dead and their return to life by Meadowlark-man, who would not permit immortality.

The creation of real people, the ancestors of the present Indians, by the transformation of feathers, sticks, or clay. [3] Of these beliefs, origin from feathers is the most distinctive

---

[3] A single exception has been found: The Northern Mewuk account for people by the gradual evolution of the offspring of the Cougar-man and his wives, the Grizzly Bear-woman and the Raccoon-woman.

19

and widespread, reaching from Fresno Creek north to Clear Lake. [4]

The completion and perfection of newly created man by the gift of five fingers from *Pe-tā'-le* the Lizard-man, who, having five himself, understood their value.

MINOR BELIEFS

In addition to the more fundamental elements of Mewan Mythology there are numerous beliefs which, while equally widespread, vary with the tribe and are of less importance. Among these are the tales of the elderberry tree – the source of music and other beneficent gifts to the people. In the beginning of the world the elderberry tree, as it swayed to and fro in the breeze, made sweet music for the Star-maidens and kept them from falling asleep; its wood served *Tol'-le-loo* for a flute when he put the Valley People to sleep so that he might steal the fire; and today it serves for flutes and clapper-sticks in nearly all the tribes and plays a vital part in their ceremonial observances.

Other widespread beliefs are that the great hunters of the FIRST PEOPLE were the Raven, Cougar, and Gray Fox; that Mermaids or Water-women, who sometimes harm people, dwell in the ocean

---

[4] The widespread belief in the origin of people from feathers accounts for the reverence shown feathers by some of the tribes. This feeling sometimes manifests itself in a great fear or dread lest the failure to show proper respect for feathers, or to observe punctiliously certain prescribed acts in connection with the use of feather articles on ceremonious occasions, be followed by illness or disaster. This awe of feathers, I have observed among the *Hoo'-koo-e'-ko* of Tomales Bay, the *Tu'-le-yo'-me* of Lake County, and the Northern *Mewuk* of Calaveras County.

and in certain rivers; that the echo is the Lizard-man talking back; that certain divinities have the magic power of accomplishing their desires by wishing; and that the red parts of birds – as the chin of the Humming-bird, the underside of the wings and tail of the western Flicker, the breast of the Robin, and the red head of the Mountain Tanager and certain others, indicate that these parts have been in contact with the fire.

LOCAL OR TRIBAL MYTHS

There are also numerous local beliefs, confined to particular tribes or groups of tribes. Thus the Inneko tribes, those living north of San Francisco Bay, tell of a flood; the two coast tribes say that in the beginning the Divinity Coyote-man came to America from the west by crossing the Pacific Ocean on a raft; the Northern Mewuk believe that they came from the Cougar-man and Grizzly Bear-woman; the Tu'-le-yo'me say that when *Sah'-te* set the world on fire, Coyote-man made the flood and put out the fire. Other local myths are that *Wek'-wek* was born of a rock; that *Chā'-ke* the Tule-wren, a poor despised orphan boy, shot out the sun, leaving the world in total darkness; that *His'-sik* the Skunk, whose greed and oppression were intolerable, was destroyed by the superior cunning of *Too'-wik* the Badger; that *He'-koo-lās* the Sun-woman owed her brilliancy to a coat of resplendent abalone shells; that the *We'-ke-wil'-lah* brothers, tiny Shrews, stole the fire from *Kah'-kah-*

21

te the Crow and by touching a bug to the spark made the first firefly. Numerous others will be found in the tales – in fact every tribe has myths of its own. Furthermore, in the general mythologies, each band or subtribe has slight variants, so that even the creation myths, as related by different bands, present minor differences.

The repeated mention in the mythologies of certain objects and practices (as the ceremonial roundhouse, the use of the stone mortar and pestle for grinding acorns, the use of baskets for cooking, the use of the bow and arrow and sling in hunting, the practice of gambling by means of the hand-game, and many others) proves that these objects and observances are not of recent introduction but were among the early possessions and practices of the Mewan tribes.

It is important to discriminate between the real mythology of a people, the tales that deal with personages and events of the very remote past, and present day myths, which deal with happenings of the hour or of the very recent past. Some of the present day myths of the Mewan tribes may be found in a separate chapter at the end of the volume.

CHARACTERISTICS OF THE FIRST PEOPLE PERPETUATED IN THEIR FINAL FORMS

The names of individual personages among the FIRST PEOPLE were carried on to the animals, objects, or forces which these people became at the time of their final transformation, and are still borne by them. Hence in the accompanying stories the names of the various animals and objects should not be understood as referring to them as they exist today but to their remote ancestors among the FIRST PEOPLE. Whatever their original form – and the Indian conception seems to picture them as half human – the distinctive attributes of the FIRST PEOPLE were in the main handed down to the animals and objects they finally became.

Thus *Oo-soom'-ma-te's* fondness for acorns was not diminished by her transformation into the Grizzly Bear; *Yu'-wel's* skill as a hunter did not forsake him when he turned into the Gray Fox; *He-le'-jah's* prowess as a deer slayer lost nothing when he changed to the Cougar; and *Too'-pe's* nocturnal ways were not abandoned when she became the Kangaroo Rat. Similarly, *Ko-to'-lah's* habit of jumping into the water is perpetuated by the Frog; *Too'-wek's* preëminence as a digger is still conspicuous in the Badger; *To-to'-ka-no's* loud penetrating voice is even now a signal characteristic of the Sandhill Crane; while the swiftness of flight of *Wek'-wek, Hoo-loo'-e*, and *Le'-che-che* who could shoot through the holes in the sky, ever opening and closing with lightning rapidity, are today marked attributes of the Falcon, Dove, and Humming-bird. So it is also with *Nuk'-kah* the Shower and *Sah'-win-ne* the Hail, who were sent to overtake and capture a fleeing enemy and who to this day are noted for the velocity and force of their movements. Such cases might be multiplied almost indefinitely.

Distribution of the Mewan Indians [5]

The territory of the Mewan tribes comprised the lower slopes and foothills of the Sierra Nevada between the Cosumnes River on the north and Fresno Creek on the south, with the adjacent plain from the foothills to Suisun Bay, and also two smaller disconnected areas north of San Francisco Bay – one in the interior, reaching from Pope Valley to the south end of Clear Lake, the other on the coast, from Golden Gate northerly nearly to the mouth of Russian River. (See accompanying map.)

At present the vanishing remnants of the Mewuk tribes are scattered over their old territory on the west flank of the Sierra; the handful that remain of the Tuleyome tribe are gathered in a small rancheria on Putah Creek in Lake County; while the sole survivors of the Hookooeko and Olamentko tribes (in each case a single person) still cling to their original homes on Tomales and Bodega Bays.

Differences in Language

The California tribes are stationary, not nomadic; they have lived for thousands of years in the places they now occupy, or did occupy until driven

[5] For a detailed account of the distribution of these tribes see my article entitled, "Distribution and Classification of the Mewan stock of California," *American Anthropologist*, vol. ix, 338-357.

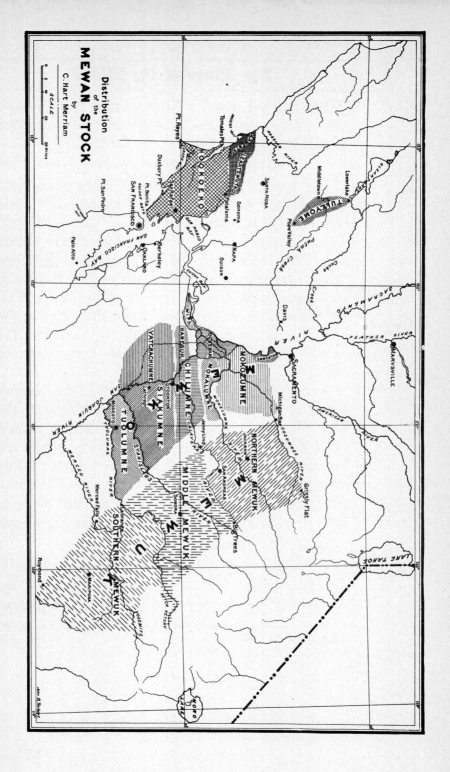

Distribution
of the
MEWAN STOCK
by
C. Hart Merriam

SCALE

away by the whites; and during this long period of isolation they have evolved different languages – for even among tribes of the same linguistic group the differences in language are often so great that members of one tribe cannot understand the speech of another.[6]

As the languages of the tribes composing the Mewan stock show varying degrees of kinship, so their myths exhibit varying relationships. Those of the Sierra region are the most closely interrelated; those of the San Francisco Bay region and northward the most divergent.

---

[6] Hence in the accompanying myths the name of the same personage or animal differs according to the tribe speaking. Thus Coyote-man may be *Ah-hä'-le, Os-sä'-le, O-lä'-choo, O-lä'-nah, O-let'-te, Ol'-le*, or *O'-ye*. Similarly, the Humming-bird may be *Koo-loo'-loo, Koo-loo'-pe*, or *Le'-che-che*. The Falcon or Duck-hawk, on the other hand, is *Wek'-wek* in all the tribes. This is because his name is derived from his cry. Many other Indian names of mammals and birds have a similar origin.

Note

THE accompanying illustrations are from paintings made expressly for the present collection of Myths by Edwin W. Deming of New York and Charles J. Hittell of San Francisco.

Of the stories here published, only a few are complete, and several consist of the merest fragments. All however are of ethnologic value, for even those expressing a single idea may prove of service in tracing relationship. In preparing them for the press my aim has been to reproduce them in simple English, adhering as closely as possible to the form in which they were told me by the Indians. Certain brief passages and repetitions have been omitted; nothing has been added.

All the Indian words, whether tribal names or names of objects, are written in simple phonetic English. The letter *a*, when unmarked, has the sound of *a* in fat; *a* long (ā) has the sound of *a* in fate; and the *ah* sound is always spelled, *ah*.

Part 1: Ancient Myths

STORIES OF THE FIRST PEOPLE – PEOPLE WHO LIVED
BEFORE REAL PEOPLE WERE CREATED

The Mewuk tribes, those inhabiting the western slopes and
foothills of the Sierra, call the ancient myths *oo'-ten-ne* or
oot'-ne, meaning the history of the FIRST PEOPLE. (The Northern Mewuk say *oo'-ten nas'-se-sa*.) In this connection it may
be significant that the name of Bower Cave, the home of *Too'-
le* and *He-le'-jah*, two great chiefs of the FIRST PEOPLE, is
Oo'-tin.

HOW WIT'-TAB-BAH THE ROBIN GOT HIS RED BREAST

FRAGMENT OF A TALE OF THE NORTHERN MEWUK
As told in the mountains near Mokelumne River

PERSONAGE

Wit'-tab-bah who became the Robin (*Planesticus migratorius propinquus*)

How Wit'=tab=bah the Robin got his Red Breast

A LONG time ago the world was dark and cold and the people had no fire. *Wit'-tab-bah* the Robin learned where the fire was and went on a far journey to get it. After he had traveled a great distance he came to the place and stole it and carried it back to the people. Every night on the way he lay with his breast over it to keep it from getting cold; this turned his breast red. Finally he reached home with it and gave it to the people. Then he made the Sun out of it, but before doing this he put some into the *oo'-noo* tree (the buckeye) so the people could get it when they needed it. From that day to this all the people have known that when they want fire they can get it by rubbing an *oo'-noo* stick against a piece of dry wood; this makes the flame come out.

How Ah-ha'-le Stole the Sun for the Valley People
A Tale of the Southern Mewuk

A long time ago there were two countries, the Valley Country and the Foothills Country, and each had its own kind of people. The Valley Country was the big flat land which the white people call the San Joaquin Plain; it had no trees and no Sun but was always enveloped in fog and was always cold and dark. The Foothills Country began on the east side of the valley and reached up into the mountains; it was covered with trees and had the Sun.

Two versions of the story have been obtained: (1) How *Ah-ha'-le* stole the Sun, told by the Mariposa Mewuk; and (2) How *Ah-ha'-le* stole the Morning, told by the Chowchilla Mewuk.

How Ah-ha'-le Stole the Sun
As told by the Mariposa Mewuk

Personages

Ah-hā'-le the Coyote-man

To-to'-kan-no Chief of the Valley People, who became the Sandhill Crane

Ah-wahn'-dah Keeper of the Sun, who became the Turtle.

How Ah-ha-le stole the Sun for the Valley People

As told by the Mariposa Mewuk

TO-TO'-KAN-NO the Sandhill Crane was chief of the Valley People and *Ah-hā'-le*, the Coyote-man lived with him. Their country was cold and dark and full of fog.

Ah-hā'le was discontented and traveled all about, trying to find a better place for the people. After a while he came to the Foothills Country where it began to be light. He went on a little farther and for the first time in his life saw trees, and found the country dry and warm, and good to look at. Soon he saw the Foothills People and found their village. He was himself a magician or witch doctor, so he turned into one of the Foothills People and mingled with them to see what they had and what they were doing. He saw that they had fire, which made light and became *Wut'-too* the Sun. He saw also that there were both men and women, that the women pounded acorns and cooked acorn mush in baskets, and that everybody ate food. He ate with them and learned that food was good.

When his belly was full he went home and told the chief *To-to'-kan-no* that he had found a good

35

3

place where there were people who had the sun
and moon and stars, and women, and things to
eat. He then asked *To-to'-kan-no*, "What are we
going to do? Are we going to stay down here in
the dark and never eat? The people up there have
wives and children; the women make acorn soup
and other things; the men have light and can see
to hunt and kill deer. We live down here in the
dark and have no women and nothing to eat.
What are we going to do?"

Chief *To-to'-kan-no* answered; "Those things
are not worth having. I don't want the Sun, nor
the light, nor any of those things. Go back up there
if you want to."

Ah-hä'le went back to the foothills and did as
he had done before, and liked the country and the
people. Then he returned and told *To-to'-kan-no*
what he had told him before, and again asked,
"What are we going to do? Can't we buy the
Sun? The people up there send the Sun away
nights so they can sleep, and it comes back every
day so they can see to hunt and get things to eat
and have a good time. I like the Sun. Let us buy
him."

To-to'-kan-no answered, "What is the matter
with you? What would you do with the Sun;
how would you use it?" But *Ah-hä'-le* was not
satisfied. He went back to the Foothills People
several times, and the more he saw of the Sun the
more he wanted it. But *To-to'-kan-no* always said

The Foothills Country. "*Ah-ha'-le* went on a little farther and for the first time in his life saw trees, and found the country dry and warm and good to look at."

he did not want it. Finally however he told *Ah-hā'-le* that he might go and find out what it would cost.

Ah-hā'le went and found that the people would not sell it; that if he got it he would have to steal it. And this would be very difficult, for *Ah-wahn'-dah* the Turtle, keeper of the Sun, was most watchful; he slept only a few minutes at a time and then stood up and looked around; besides, when he slept he always kept one eye open. If *Ah-hā'-le* moved his foot *Ah-wahn'-dah* would pick up his bow and arrow. *Ah-hā'le* felt discouraged and did not know what to do. He feared that in order to get the Sun he would have to take *Ah-wahn'-dah* also.

But he decided to try once more, so he went again and turned into a man of the Foothills People. About four o'clock in the afternoon all the hunters went off to hunt deer. Then *Ah-hā'-le* turned into a big oak limb and fell down on the trail, and wished that *Ah-wahn'-dah* the Sun's keeper would come along first. And so it happened, for soon *Ah-wahn'-dah* came along the trail, saw the crooked limb, picked it up, carried it home on his shoulder, and threw it down on the ground. After supper he picked it up again and threw it against the fire, but it would not lay flat for it was very crooked and always turned up. Finally *Ah-wahn'-dah* threw it right into the middle of the fire. Then he looked all around, but could not see anybody. *Ah-hā'le* who was now in the fire did not burn, but kept perfectly still and wished the keeper, *Ah-wahn'-dah*, would go to sleep.

Soon this happened and *Ah-wahn'-dah* fell fast asleep. Then *Ah-hā'-le* changed back into his own form and seized the Sun and ran quickly away with it.

Ah-wahn'-dah awoke and saw that the Sun was gone and called everybody to come quick and find it, but they could not for *Ah-hā'-le* had taken it down through the fog to the Valley People.

But when the Valley People saw it they were afraid and turned away from it, for it was too bright and hurt their eyes, and they said they could never sleep.

Ah-hā'le took it to the chief, *To-to'-kan-no*, but *To-to'-kan-no* would not have it; he said he didn't understand it; that *Ah-hā'-le* must make it go, for he had seen how the Foothills People did it.

When *To-to'-kan-no* refused to have anything to do with the Sun, *Ah-hā'-le* was disappointed, for he had worked very hard to get it.

Still he said, "Well, I'll make it go."

So he carried the Sun west to the place where the sky comes down to the earth, and found the west hole in the sky, and told *Wut'-too* to go through the hole and down under the earth and come up on the east side and climb up through the east hole in the sky, and work in two places – to make light over the Foothills People first, then come on down and make light over the Valley People, and then go

The Valley People shrinking from the Light. "*Ah-ha-le* stole the
Sun and brought it down through the fog and darkness to the
Valley People, but they were afraid and turned from it."

through the west hole again and back under the earth so the people could sleep, and to keep on doing this, traveling all the time.

Wut'-too the Sun did as he was told. Then *To-to'-kan-no* and all the Valley People were glad, because they could see to hunt, and the Foothills People were satisfied too, for they had the light in the daytime so they could see, and at night the Sun went away so all the people could sleep.

After this, when the Sun was in the sky as it is now, all the FIRST PEOPLE turned into animals.

How Ah-ha'-le stole the Morning

As told by the Chowchilla Mewuk

PERSONAGES

Ah-hā'-le the Coyote-man

We'-wis-sool Chief of the Valley People, who became the Golden Eagle [7]

Ah-wahn'-dah Keeper of the Morning, who became the Turtle

---

[7] The word *We'-wis-sool* or *We'-wŭ-sool* is not of Mewan origin but is borrowed from the Yokut tribes immediately to the south – the Chuk-chan'-sy and Kosh-sho'-o. In the Mewuk language the Golden Eagle is called *We'-pi-ahk* or *We-pi-ah'-gah.*

How Ah=ha=le stole the Morning

As told by the Chowchilla Mewuk

IN the long ago time the world was dark and
there was no fire. The only light was the
Morning,[8] and it was so far away in the high
mountains of the east that the people could not see
it; they lived in total darkness. The chief *We'-
wis-sool*, the Golden Eagle, felt very badly because
it was always dark and cried all the time.

Ah-hā'-le the Coyote-man made up his mind to
go and get the Morning in order that the people
might have light. So he set out on the long journey to the east, up over the high mountains, saying,
"I'm going to get the Morning."

Finally he came to *Ah-wahn'-dah* the Turtle.
Ah-wahn'-dah was guardian of the Morning; he
wore a big basket on his back. When *Ah-hā'-le*
came close to *Ah-wahn'-dah* he was afraid something would catch him and carry him off. He said
to himself, "I'm going to turn myself into a log of
wood so I'll be too heavy to be carried off," and he
turned into a big dry limb. *Ah-wahn'-dah* the
Turtle put fire to the limb, but it would not burn;
then he fell asleep.

---

[8] Morning, in this story, is obviously synonymous with sun and
light, and probably with fire also, as in the preceding story.

When the Guardian had gone to sleep *Ah-hā'-le* got up and said, "Now I'm going to get the Morning." So he changed back into his own form and put out his foot and touched the Morning, and it growled. He then caught hold of it and jumped quickly and ran away with it and brought it back to his people.

When he arrived he said to *We'-wis-sool* the Eagle, "How are you?"

We'-wis-sool answered, "All right," but was still crying because it was dark.

Then *Ah-hā'-le* said, "Tomorrow morning it is going to be light," but *We'-wis-sool* did not believe him.

In the morning *Ah-hā'-le* gave the people the light. *We'-wis-sool* was very happy and asked *Ah-hā'-le* where he got it, and *Ah-hā'-le* told him. Then the people began to walk around and find things to eat, for now they could see.

How Tol'-le-loo got the Fire for the Mountain People

A Tale of the Northern Mewuk

The Mountain People lived in the Sierra near the Moke-lumne River, which they called *Ut'-ta Wah-kah'-loo*, meaning big river. They had no fire and the world was dark.

The Valley People lived on the San Joaquin Plain, which they called *Ol-law'-win*. Their roundhouse was not far from the spot now occupied by the city of Stockton. They had a small fire in the middle of the roundhouse and *Wit'-tab-bah* the Robin was its keeper.

Personages

O-lā'-choo the Coyote-man

Tol'-le-loo the flute-player who became the White-footed Mouse

Wek'-wek a Chief of the Valley People, who became the Falcon

We-pi-ah'-gah a Chief of the Valley People, who became the Golden Eagle

Mol'-luk who became the Condor

Hoo'-a-zoo who became the Turkey Buzzard

Hoo-loo'-e who became the Dove

Te-wi'-yu who became the Red-shafted Flicker

Wit'-tab-bah Keeper of the Fire, who became the Robin

Hah-ki'-ah who became the Elk

Hal'-loo-zoo who became the Antelope

Sahk'-mum-chah who became the Cinnamon Bear

Le'-che-che who became the Humming-bird

Le-che-koo'-tah-mah who became another small bird with a long bill

48

How Tol-le-loo got the Fire for the Mountain People

WEK'-WEK the Falcon and *We'-pi-ah'-gah* the Golden Eagle were Chiefs of the Valley People. Among the members of their tribe were *Mol'-luk* the Condor; *Hoo'-a-zoo* the Turkey Buzzard; *Hoo-loo'-e* the Dove; *Te-wi'-yu* the Red-shafted Flicker, who must have been very close to the fire as any one can see from the red under his wings and tail, and *Wit'-tab-bah* the red-breasted Robin, who was keeper of the fire. There were also *Hah-ki'-ah* the Elk, *Hal'-loo-zoo* the Antelope, *Sahk'-mum-chah* the Cinnamon Bear, and others.

The Mountain People were in darkness and wanted fire but did not know where it was or how to get it. *O-lā'-choo* the Coyote-man tried hard to find it but did not succeed. After a while *Tol'-le-loo* the White-footed Mouse discovered the fire and the Mountain People sent him to steal it.

Tol'-le-loo took his flute (*loo'-lah*) of elderberry wood and went down into the valley and found the big roundhouse of *Wek'-wek* and *We-pi-ah'-gah* and began to play. The people liked the music and asked him to come inside. So he went in and played for them. Soon all the people felt

49

sleepy. *Wit'-tab-bah* the Robin was sure that *Tol'-le-loo* had come to steal the fire, so he spread himself over it and covered it all up in order to hide it, and it turned his breast red. But *Tol'-le-loo* kept on playing his flute and in a little while all the people were sound asleep; even *Wit'-tab-bah* could not keep awake.

Then *Tol'-le-loo* ran up to *Wit'-tab-bah* and cut a little hole in his wing and crawled through and stole the fire and put it inside his flute. When he had done this he ran out with it and climbed up to the top of the high mountain called *Oo'-yum-bel'-le* (Mount Diablo) and made a great fire which lighted up all the country till even the blue mountains far away in the east [the Sierra Nevada range] could be seen. Before this all the world was dark.

When *Wek'-wek* awoke he saw the fire on *Oo'-yum-bel'-le* and knew that *Tol'-le-loo* had stolen it. So he ran out and followed him and after a while caught him.

Tol'-le-loo said, "Look and see if I have the fire."

Wek'-wek looked but could not find it, for it was inside the flute. Then *Wek'-wek* pitched *Tol'-le-loo* into the water and let him go.

Tol'-le-loo got out and went east into the mountains and carried the fire in his flute to the Mountain People; then he took it out of the flute and put it on the ground and covered it with leaves and pine needles and tied it up in a small bundle.

Tol'-le-loo the Mouse playing his Flute and putting the Valley People to sleep so that he can steal the Fire

O-lā'-choo the Coyote smelled it and wanted to steal it. He came up and pushed it with his nose and was going to swallow it when it suddenly shot up into the sky and became the Sun.

O-lā'-choo sent *Le'-che-che* the Humming-bird, and another bird, named *Le-che-koo'-tah-mah*, who also had a long bill, after it, but they could not catch it and came back without it.

The people took the fire that was left and put it into two trees, *oo'-noo* the buckeye and *mon'-o-go* the incense cedar, where it still is and where it can be had by anyone who wants it.

NOTE – This story has been told me by several Mewuk Indians independently. The only variation of consequence is that, in one version, *Wek'-wek* and *We-pi-ah'-gah* gave a feast and invited the Mountain People to come; and it was while they were there that *Tol'-le-loo* put the Valley People to sleep with his flute and ran off with the fire. The story is called *Oo'-ten-nas'-se-sa*, though of course this is only a part.

WHY THE LIZARD MAN DID NOT RESTORE DEAD PEOPLE TO LIFE

Outline of Creation Myth of the Northern Mewuk as related at Wal'le in the upper foothills immediately south of the Mokelumne River

PERSONAGES
Oo-soo'-ma-te the Grizzly Bear-woman
Hoi-ah'-ko the First People
Pe-ta'-lit-te the Little Lizard-man
Suk'-ka-de the Black Lizard-man
Yu'-kah-loo the Meadowlark-man

Followed by a corresponding myth of the *Pä'-we-nan* tribe of Midoo stock from *Poo-soo'-ne*, at the junction of the American River with the Sacramento.

54

Why the Lizard Man did not restore Dead People to Life

OO-SOO'-MA-TE the Grizzly Bear and *Hoi-ah' ko* the First People made the first Mewuk [Indian people]. When the Mewuk were made they had no hands to take hold of things. Then *Pe-tā'-lit-te* the Little Lizard and *Suk'-ka-de* the Black Lizard gave them hands with five fingers.

When the first Mewuk [Indian] died,*Suk'-ka-de* the Black Lizard was sorry and set to work to bring him back to life. But *Yu'-kah-loo* the Meadowlark came and drove him away, saying, "*Mewuk ut'-tud-dah, Mewuk tuk'-tuk-ko*" – meaning, People no good, people smell.

NOTE – The *Pă'-we-nan,* who lived on the Sacramento and Feather Rivers from the Junction of American River northward nearly to the Yuba, hold a belief which, while in some respects strikingly similar, is in other respects widely different. They say:

In the beginning *Hi'-kaht* the great chief said that when a person died, he should come to life on the fourth day thereafter, and should live again.

Then *Hool* the Meadowlark-man said No; he

55

did not want *Nis'-se-nan'* [people] to live again after they were dead. He said *Nis'-se-nan'* were no good and by and by would smell; they had better stay dead.

Yawm the Coyote-man agreed with *Hool* the Meadowlark-man – he did not want people to live again; he wanted them to stay dead.

Yawm the Coyote-man had a daughter of whom he was very fond.

Hi'-kaht the great chief, after hearing *Yawm* say that he wanted people to stay dead after they died, went out into the brush and took a branch of a plant called *Sak-ki-ak* and laid it in the trail. In the night the plant turned into *Koi'-maw* the rattlesnake. The next morning *Yawm's* daughter came along the trail and *Koi'-maw* bit her and she died.

Yawm the Coyote-man found the dead body of his daughter and felt badly. He picked her up and said, "In four days you will come to life again."

But *Hi'-kaht* replied, "No, she will not come to life again. You said that when people died you wanted them to stay dead. So your daughter will stay dead and will not live again."

This is the reason why everybody stays dead after they die and nobody lives again.

The Coyote and the Lizard

Fragment of a Creation Story of the Northern Mewuk

From Aw'kim in the upper foothills between Middle and
South Forks of Cosumnes River

Personages

O-lā'-choo the Coyote-man
Pe-tā'-le the Lizard-man
Yu'-ka-loo the Meadowlark-man

With a note on a Southern Nissenan creation myth in
which the Moon figures as one of the early divinities

Che Coyote and the Lizard

O-LA'-CHOO the Coyote-man and *Pe-tā'-le* the little Lizard-man made the world and everything in it.

After they had done this, *Pe-tā'-le* wanted to turn into the Moon but *O-lā'-choo* the Coyote-man and *Yu'-ka-loo* the Meadowlark-man would not allow him to do so. [9]

[9] This reference to the moon is the only one I have discovered among the Mewuk creation myths. But the next people on the north – the Nissenan – count the Moon-man among the early divinities. The Southern Nissenan give the following account of the creation of man:

In the beginning, *Pombok* the Moon-man, *O'-leh* the Coyote-man, and *Pit-chak* the Lizard-man decided to make people but differed as to what the first man should be like, for each of the three wanted man to be like himself.

After they had argued a long time they finally agreed that man should have a round face like the Moon-man, but they could not agree as to his hands. Coyote-man insisted that he should have paws like his own, but Lizard-man said that paws would be of no use – that man should have five fingers so he could take hold of things. Finally Lizard-man carried his point and gave man five long fingers like his own.

Coyote-man never forgave him, and to this day the Coyote hunts the lizard and kills him whenever he can.

59

How the People got Five Fingers; How they Obtained Fire; and How they Broke up into Tribes

Creation Story of the Middle Mewuk

As told at *Ta'-la-sā'-na* in the Tuolumne foothills near Bald Rock

Personages

Os-sā'-le the Coyote-man, whose name was changed to *Kat'-wah*

Pe-tā'-le the Little Lizard who gave man five fingers
Loo'-loo-e the White-footed Mouse, who stole the fire
We-pi-ah'-gah the Golden Eagle, chief of the Valley People
Wek'-wek the Falcon
Sah'-win-ne the Hail Storm
Nuk'-kah the Thunder Shower

How the People got Five Fingers; How they obtained Fire; and How they broke up into Tribes

ALL the world was dark.

Os-sā'-le the Coyote-man and *Pe-tā'-le* the Lizard-man were First People. They tried to make Indian people, each like himself. *Os-sā'-le* said he was going to make man just like himself.

Pe-tā'-le said that would be absurd; "How could man eat or take hold of anything if he had no fingers?"

So they quarrelled, and *Os-sā'-le* tried to kill *Pe-tā'-le*; but *Pe-tā'-le* slid into a crack in a rock where *Os-sā'-le* could not reach him. Then they talked and argued for a long time. After a while *Pe-tā'-le* came out ahead and when they made people he gave them five fingers.

The world was dark and everybody wanted light and fire. By and by *Pe-tā'-le* the Lizard said, "I see smoke down in the valley; who will go and get it. *Loo'-loo-e* the White-footed Mouse runs fast and plays the flute well; he had better go." So *Loo'-loo-e* went with his flute (*loo'-lah*) and found the home of the Valley People and played for them. They liked his music and gave a big feast and asked him to come into the roundhouse and play so that everyone might hear him.

We'-pi-ah'-gah the Eagle was chief of the Valley People and *Wek'-wek* the Falcon lived with him. When all the people had assembled and *Loo'-loo-e* the Mouse was there with his flute, Captain *We-pi-ah'-gah* took the big feather blanket called *kook'-si-u*, made of feathers of *Mol'-luk* the Condor, and closed the doorway with it and made it very tight, for he had a feeling that *Loo'-loo-e* might try to steal something and run off with it.

Then *Loo'-loo-e* took his flute and began to play; he lay on his back and rocked to and fro and played for a long time. Everyone liked the music and felt happy. In a little while they all became sleepy. Soon *Loo'-loo-e* looked around and saw that they were asleep; but he kept on playing till everybody was sound asleep. Then he got up and went to the fire and stole it all – two small coals – and put them in his flute and started to run away. But he could not get out of the roundhouse because of the thick feather blanket which *We-pi-ah'-gah* had hung over the doorway. So he stopped and cut a hole through it with his teeth and then ran out and hurried toward the mountains.

After a while the people awoke and found that the fire was gone. They were sure that *Loo'-loo-e* the Mouse had stolen it, and said, "Whom can we send who is fast enough to overtake him? Of all our people only *Sah'-win-ne* the Hail and *Nuk'-kah* the Shower are fast enough." So they sent these two to catch him. They rushed off toward the mountains and overtook him.

He saw them coming and put one coal in the *oo'-noo* tree (buckeye) and threw the other in the water. When *Sah'-win-ne* and *Nuk'-kah* caught him they could not find the coals. He told them to look, he had nothing. They looked and found nothing, and went back and told the Valley People.

Then *Loo'-loo-e* took the coal from the *oo'noo* tree and put it back in his flute and ran up into the mountains with it and gave it to his people, and they put it in the middle of the roundhouse. Before this their country was dark, and they had always eaten their food raw. Now they could see and could cook meat.

Then *Os-sā'-le* the Coyote-man brought the intestines of a deer and put them on the fire, covering it up and nearly putting it out. Because of his selfishness in doing this the people changed his name from *Os-sā'-le* to *Kat'-wah* (greedy), which they call him to this day.

Then the people felt cold and only those in the middle of the roundhouse could talk as they had talked before. Those around the sides were so cold that their teeth chattered and they could not talk plainly. They separated into four groups on the four sides of the house – one on the north, one

on the south, one on the east, and one on the west –
and each group began to speak differently from the
others, and also differently from the one in the
middle. This is the way the speech of the people
began to break up into five languages, and this is
the way the five tribes [10] began – the people being
driven apart by the selfishness of Coyote.

---

[10] The *Me'wah* knew only five tribes: their own; the people to the
north, whom they call *Tam'-moo-lek* or *Tah-mah-lā'-ko* (from *Tah'-mah*, north); those on the east, whom they call *Mo'-nok* or *He'-sah-duk*
(from *He'-sum*, east); those on the south, whom they call *Choo'-mat-tuk*
(from *Choo'-match*, south), and those on the west, whom they call
O'-loo-kuk or *Ol'-lo-kuk* (from *O'-lo-win* or *Ol'-lo-win*, meaning down
west – in the valley).

The Birth of Wek'-wek and the Creation of Man

The Hool-poom'-ne Story of Creation

The Hool-poom'-ne lived on the east side of the lower Sacramento River, beginning a few miles below the place where the city of Sacramento now stands. They are now extinct.

Personages

O-let'-te Coyote-man, the Creator
Mol'-luk the Condor, father of *Wek'-wek*
Wek'-wek the Falcon, son of *Mol'-luk* and grandson of *O-let'-te*
Hul'-luk mi-yum'-ko the two beautiful women chiefs of the Star-people
Os-so-so'-li Pleiades, one of the Star-women
Ke'-lok the North Giant
Hoo-soo'-pe the Mermaids or Water-maidens, sisters of *Wek'-wek*
Choo'-hoo the Turkey Buzzard
Kok'-kol the Raven
Ah-wet'-che the Crow
Koo-loo'-loo the Humming-bird

Fragment of Version told by the Hoo'-koo-e-ko of Tomales Bay

Personages

O'-ye the Coyote-man
Wek'-wek the Falcon
Koo-loo'-pis the Humming-bird

The Birth of Wek-wek and the Creation of Man

IN the beginning there was a huge bird of the vulture kind whose name was *Mol'-luk*, the California Condor. His home was on the mountain called *Oo'-yum-bel'-le* (Mount Diablo), whence he could look out over the world – westerly over San Francisco Bay and the great ocean; easterly over the tules and the broad flat Joaquin Valley.

Every morning *Mol'-luk* went off to hunt, and every evening he came back to roost on a large rock on the east side of the mountain. One morning he noticed that something was the matter with the rock, but did not know what the trouble was, or what to do for it. So he went off to consult the doctors. The doctors were brothers, two dark snipe-like little birds who lived on a small creek near the foot of the mountain. He told them his rock was sick and asked them to go with him, and led them to it. When they saw the rock they said, "The rock is your wife; she is going to give you a child;" and added, "we must make a big fire." Then all three set to work packing wood; they worked hard and brought a large quantity and made a big fire. Then they took hold of the rock, tore it loose, rolled it into the fire, and piled more wood around it. When the rock became hot, it burst open with a great noise, and from the inside out darted *Wek'-wek* the Falcon. As he came out he said '*wek*' and passed on swiftly without stopping. He flew over all the country – north, south, east, and west – to see what it was like.

At that time there were no people. And there were no elderberry trees except a single one far away to the east in the place where the Sun gets up. There, in a den of rattlesnakes on a round topped hill grew *lah'-pah* the elderberry tree. Its branches, as they swayed in the wind, made a sweet musical sound. The tree sang; it sang all the time, day and night, and the song was good to hear. *Wek'-wek* looked and listened and wished he could have the tree. Near by he saw two *Hol-luk'-ki* or Star-people, and as he looked he perceived that they were the *Hul-luk mi-yum'-ko* – the great and beautiful women-chiefs of the Star-people. One was the Morning Star, the other Pleiades *Os-so-so'-li*. They were watching and working close by the elderberry tree. *Wek'-wek* liked the music and asked the Star-women about it. They told him that the tree whistled songs that kept them awake all day and all night so they could work all the time and never grow sleepy. They had the rattlesnakes to keep the birds from carrying off the elderberries.

Then *Wek'-wek* returned to his home on *Oo-yum-bel'-le* (Mount Diablo) and told *Mol'-luk* his

Mol'-luk the Condor looking off over the World from his Rock on
Mount Diablo

father what he had seen. He said he had seen the beautiful Star-women and had heard the soft whistling song of the elderberry tree that keeps one from feeling sleepy. He asked his father how they could get the music tree and have it at their home on *Oo'-yum-bel'-le*.

Mol'-luk answered, "My son, I do not know; I am not very wise; you will have to ask your grandfather; he knows everything."

"Where is my grandfather?" asked *Wek'-wek*.

"He is by the ocean," *Mol'-luk* replied.

"I never saw him," said *Wek'-wek*.

His father asked, "Didn't you see something like a stump bobbing in the water and making a noise as it went up and down?"

"Yes," said *Wek'-wek*, "I saw that."

"Well," replied *Mol'-luk*, "that is your grandfather."

"How can I get him?" asked *Wek'-wek*.

"You can't get all of him, but perhaps you can break off a little piece and in that way get him."

So *Wek'-wek* flew off to the ocean, found the stump bobbing in the water, and tore off a little piece and brought it home. When he awoke next morning the little piece had changed into *O-let'-te*, the Coyote-man, who was already living in a little house of his own on top of the mountain. *O-let'-te* told *Wek'-wek* that he was his grandfather.

Wek'-wek told *Mol'-luk* his father and added, "Now I've got my grandfather."

71

Mol'-luk replied, "Ask him what you want to know; he knows everything."

So *Wek'-wek* asked *O-let'-te*, "How are we going to get the elderberry music?"

"*Ho-ho*," answered *O-let'-te*, "that is very difficult; you might have bad luck and might be killed."

But *Wek'-wek* continued, "I want it."

Then the wise *O-let'-te* said: "All right, go and buy it, but mind what I tell you or you will be killed. You will find the Star-women pleasant and pretty. They will want you to stay and play with them. If you do so, you will die. Go and do as I tell you."

So *Wek'-wek* went. He flew fast and far – far away to the east, to the place where the Sun gets up. There he found *Hul-luk mi-yum'-ko* the Star-women and *lah'-pah* the elderberry tree. The Star-women were people of importance; both were chiefs. *Wek'-wek* had taken with him long strings of *haw'-wut*, the shell money, which as he flew streamed out behind. This he gave them for the elderberry music. The Star-women liked the *haw'-wut* and accepted it and led *Wek'wek* to the elderberry tree and told him to break off a little piece and take it home and he would have all. But when he reached the tree the rattlesnakes stood up all around and hissed at him to frighten him, for he was a stranger. The Star-women told him not to be afraid, they would drive the snakes away. So they scolded the snakes and sent them down into

72

their holes. Then *Wek'-wek* took his *soo'-pe* [digging stick] and pried off a piece of the tree. The Star-women began to play with him and wanted him to stay with them, but remembering what *O-let'-te* his grandfather had told him, he paid no attention to them but took the piece of elderberry tree and carried it swiftly home to *Oo-yum-bel'le*.

When he arrived he said to *O-let'-te*, "Grandfather, I've brought the music-tree; what shall we do with it so we can have the music?"

O-let'-te laughed as he replied, "Do you really think you have it?"

"Yes," answered *Wek'-wek*, "here it is."

Then *O-let'-te* said, "We must put it in the ground over all the country to furnish music for the *Mew'-ko* [Indian people] we are going to make, for pretty soon we shall begin to make the people."

Wek'-wek answered "Yes," but thought he would wait and see who was the smarter, himself or *O-let'-te* – for he felt very proud because he had brought the music tree.

Then they went out and traveled over all the country and planted the elderberry tree so that by and by it would furnish music and food and medicine for the Indian people they were going to make. *O-let'-te* told *Wek'-wek* that the berries would make food, the roots and blossoms medicine, and the hollow branches music.

73

Ke=lok and his Han=na=boo

WHEN *Wek'-wek* and *O-let'-te* were out hunting one day they went to *Tah-lah'-wit* the North and came to a rocky hill where they saw a great and powerful giant named *Ke'-lok*, sitting by his *han-nā'-boo* or roundhouse. *Wek'-wek* flew close to him and saw him well.

That night, when they had gone home, *Wek'-wek* said to *O-let'-te*, "Grandfather, I want to play *al'-leh* (the hand-game) with *Ke'-lok*." [11]

When *O-let'-te* heard *Wek'-wek* say he wanted to play *al'-leh* with *Ke'-lok* he laughed and said, "You! play hand-game with the Giant *Ke'-lok*!"

"Yes," answered *Wek'-wek*, "I want to play hand-game with *Ke'-lok*."

Then his grandfather told him that *Ke'-lok* was his elder brother.

"All right," said *Wek'-wek*, "I'm going to play *al'-leh* with my brother."

After a while *Wek'-wek* arrived at *Ke'-lok's* han-nā'-boo, and when *Ke'-lok* came out, said to him, "Brother, I have come to play hand-game with you."

---

[11] Nowadays *al'-leh* is a guessing game, played with two small bones, one wrapped or 'dressed' to distinguish it from the other. But in those days it was different, for *al'-leh* was played by hurling rocks with intent to kill.

75

"All right," answered *Ke'-lok*, and he at once built a fire and put eight round rocks in it and heated them until they were red hot. Then he said, "My young brother, you begin first."

"No," replied *Wek'-wek*, "I want to see you play first; you begin."

"All right," said *Ke'-lok*, and he immediately sprang up and darted up into the sky, for he was great and powerful and could do all things. As he went up he made a loud noise. Then he came down in a zig-zag course, and as he came, sang a song.

Then *Wek'-wek* began to throw hot rocks at him but purposely missed him, for he did not want to kill his brother. His grandfather *O-let'-te* the Coyote-man, called out to him from the south that if he hit *Ke'-lok* in his body it would not kill him, but that his heart (*wus'-ke*) was in his arm, under a white spot on the underside of the arm, and that if he hit that spot it would kill him; that was the only place on his body where a blow would kill him.

Wek'-wek answered, "I can easily hit that, but I don't want to kill him."

So he threw all the hot stones but took care not to hit the white spot under the arm. When he had fired all the rocks he picked them up and put them back in the fire to heat again.

Then it was *Ke'-lok's* turn.

When *Ke'-lok* was ready, *Wek'-wek* said, "All right, I will go now," and he shot up into the sky,

The Giant *Ke'-lok* hurling hot Rocks at *Wek'-wek*

making a great noise, just as *Ke'-lok* had done. Then he came down slowly, singing a song, and came toward *Ke'-lok's* roundhouse.

Then *Ke'-lok* began to throw the hot rocks at him and tried hard to hit him. But *Wek'-wek* dodged them easily and called out to *O-let'-te* his grandfather: "He can't hit me unless I let him; see me let him hit me"—for he thought he would not really be killed, believing that the magic of *O-let'-te* would keep him alive. So he let *Ke'-lok* hit him with the last rock.

Ke'-lok did hit him and he fell dead. Then *Ke'-lok* picked him up and hung him on his *ha-nā'-boo*.

Ke'-lok's place was at *Tah-lah'-wit*, the north. When *Wek'-wek* set out to go there, his grandfather *O-let'-te* had told him to pluck out and take with him one of his father's long wing-feathers and stand it up on top of *Ke'-lok's han-nā'-boo* so it could be seen a long way off. *O-let'-te* said the feather would stand so long as *Wek'wek* was alive, but if he was killed it would fall. While the hand-game was going on *O-let'-te* watched the feather, and when *Wek'-wek* was hit he saw it fall. Then he felt very sad and cried and told *Mol'-luk, Wek'-wek's* father, and they both mourned and cried.

Then *O-let'-te* said to *Mol'-luk*, "I'm going to play hand-game with *Ke'-lok*." So he took a long walking stick with a sharp point at one end and set out on the far journey to *Tah-lah'-wit*. When he arrived at *Ke'lok's han-nā'-boo* he said, "Well, how are you getting along?"

Ke'-lok answered, "I'm getting along all right."

Then *O-let'-te* said, "I have come to play hand-game."

"All right," replied *Ke'-lok*; and he built a fire and heated the rocks red hot, just as he had done before. When the rocks were hot he asked, "Who will play first?"

O-let'-te answered, "I'm an old man, but I'll go first." So he shot up into the sky with a great noise, just as *Ke'-lok* and *Wek'-wek* had done before; and then circled around and came down slowly, singing a song of his own—different from the songs the others had sung.

Then *Ke'-lok* began picking up the hot rocks and throwing them at him. But *O-let'-te*, in spite of his age, was very agile and dodged all of the eight rocks so that not one hit him.

When *Ke'-lok* had fired all the rocks he said to himself, "Maybe my grandfather will beat me after all; I feel now that I am done for," and he was afraid.

O-let'-te, who was still in the air, then came down and said, "I'm old and tired of playing that way. Do you think old people can beat young people? I don't know, but I'll try anyhow."

It was now *Ke'-lok's* turn to go up and *O-let'-te's* turn to throw the hot rocks. *Ke'-lok* sprang up in the same way as before, and came down in the same way, singing his own song. *O-let'-te* picked up the hot stones and threw them at *Ke'-lok*, one after the other, until he had thrown four, but did not try to hit him. He then looked toward *Ke'-lok's* han-nā'-boo and saw *Wek'-wek* hanging there, and was very angry. When he picked up the fifth stone he said, "Now I am going to hit the white spot on his arm, over his heart," and he fired the rock straight and hit the white spot, and *Ke'-lok* fell dead.

As soon as *Ke'-lok* was dead his fire sprang up and began to burn and spread. Then *O-let'-te* went to *Wek'-wek* and took him in his hands. *Wek'-wek's* feathers moved a little; then his head drew in a little; then his eyes opened and he stood up and came to life and exclaimed, "The country is burning!"

And so it was, for the fire was now sweeping fiercely over the land, spreading swiftly to the east and west and south, roaring with a mighty roar, consuming everything in its way and filling the air with flame and smoke.

O-let'-te directed *Wek'-wek* to fly quickly to the ocean and dive under the water, where he had two sisters named *Hoo-soo'-pe* [12] (the Mermaids), and stay with them while the world was burning. So *Wek'-wek* went into the ocean and found his sisters and remained with them until the fire had burnt over all the land and had burnt itself out. While with them he killed a great many ducks. His

[12] See the story of *Ho-hā'-pe*, page 238.

sisters did not like him to kill ducks, so after they had spoken to him he killed only what he needed to eat.

The Creation of Man

AFTER a while the world cooled off and
Wek'-wek came back to *Oo'-yum-bel'-
le* (Mount Diablo) to see his father *Mol'-
luk* and his grandfather *O-let'te*. He said to *Mol'-
luk*, "O father;" and *Mol'-luk* answered, " What is
it my son?"

Wek'-wek asked, " How can we make *Mew'-ko*
(Indian people) and have them in the country?"

His father replied, " I cannot tell you; ask your
grandfather, he can tell you."

So *Wek'-wek* asked his grandfather, *O-let'-te*,
how they were going to make people.

O-let'-te answered, "Hah-hah, it will take you
a good while to do that. If you are going to do
that you must have a head. If people are coming
you must first put out [provide] everything everywhere so they can live. If you want to do this I
will think about it."

" I want to see it done," answered *Wek'-wek*.

"All right," said *O-let'-te*, " I know how. I
must catch the three birds – *Choo'-hoo* the Turkey
Buzzard, *Kok'-kol* the Raven, and *Ah-wet'-che* the
Crow. The only way to catch these birds is to
make-believe dead."

So *Wek'-wek* and *O-let'-te* went out on the plain

83

together and *O-let'-te* lay down on the ground and pretended he was dead. He opened his mouth and let his tongue out and relaxed himself so *Choo'-hoo* the Buzzard would think he was dead. He told *Wek'-wek* he would call if he caught the birds; and *Wek'-wek* went away.

Soon *Choo'-hoo* the Turkey Buzzard came sailing over and saw the dead Coyote-man and circled around and lit on the ground beside him. *Kok'-kol* the Raven and *Ah-wet'-che* the Crow saw *Choo'-hoo* go down and knew that he had found something to eat, so they too hastened to the place. Just as all three began to eat, *O-let'-te* suddenly sprang up and caught them. He then called *Wek'-wek* to come, and told him to pick off the feathers and be careful not to lose a single one. This *Wek'-wek* did; he picked all the feathers from the three birds and took them all home.

Then he asked his grandfather, "What are we going to do next?"

"Make people," answered *O-let'-te*.

"All right," said *Wek'-wek*, "do you know how?"

"Yes," answered *O-let'-te*.

Wek'-wek then told *Mol'-luk* his father that they were going to make people. *Mol'-luk* answered, "All right."

Next morning *O-let'-te* and *Wek'-wek* took the feathers and traveled over all the country. They picked out the places where they wanted Indian villages to be, and in each place stuck up three

feathers—one for *Chā'-kah* the Chief, one for *Mi'-yum*, the head woman or Woman Chief, and one for *Soo-lā-too* the poor. And they gave each place its name—the name it has always had and bears today.

The next morning the three feathers at each place stood up and came to life and became *Mew'-ko* [Indian People]. This is the way people were made in the beginning and this is the way all the different rancherias or villages were named.

After that *O-let'-te* said to *Wek'-wek*, "Now we also are going to change; I am going to be a hunting animal and you are going to be a hunting bird." So *O-let'-te* the Coyote-man, whose form up to this time we do not know, changed to the Coyote, a furry hunting animal and became the first furry animal. And *Wek'-wek* changed to the Falcon, a hunting bird.

How they got the Fire

THE first fire was made by the Doctor Birds at the birth of *Wek'-wek*. The next fire was made by *Ke'-lok* the North Giant. After *Ke'-lok's* death and after his fire had burnt up the world and had burnt itself out, there was no fire except that of the *Hul-luk mi-yum'-ko,* the Star-women, which was close by the elderberry tree, way off in the east where the Sun gets up.

O-let'-te said to his grandson, *Wek'-wek*: "Now we have people, and elderberry music for the people, but we have no fire for them to cook with; the Star-women have it; we must steal it."

"How?" asked *Wek'-wek*.

" Send *Koo-loo'-loo* the Humming-bird; he is faster than you. Tell him to catch a little spark and bring it quickly," replied *O-let'-te*.

"All right," answered *Wek'-wek*, and he sent *Koo-loo'-loo* to fetch the fire. *Koo-loo'-loo* shot out swiftly and soon reached the Star-women by the elderberry tree in the far east, in the place where the Sun gets up. Here he hid and watched and waited, and when he saw a little spark of fire, he darted in and seized it and brought it back quickly to *Wek'-wek* and *O-let'-te*. He held it tight under his chin, and to this day if you look under the Humming-bird's chin you will see the mark of the fire.

Then *Wek'-wek* asked: "Where shall we put it?"

O-let'-te answered, "Let us put it in *oo'-noo*, the buckeye tree, where all the people can get it." So they put it in *oo'-noo*, the buckeye tree, and even now whenever an Indian wants fire he goes to the *oo'-noo* tree and gets it.

FRAGMENT OF A HOO'-KOO-E'-KO VERSION

I have discovered fragments of a similar myth among the nearly extinct *Hoo'-koo-e'-ko* north of San Francisco Bay. These people state that *O'-ye* the Coyote-man sent *Koo-loo'-pis* the Humming-bird far away to the east to steal the fire; that he brought it back to Coyote-man, and that Coyote-man put it into the buckeye tree. They state also that *Wek'-wek* once went a long way off and was killed, and that his grandfather, *O'-ye* the Coyote-man, went after him and restored him to life.

HOW KAH'-KOOL THE RAVEN BECAME A GREAT HUNTER

A TALE OF THE SOUTHERN MEWUK
As told by the Mariposa Mewuk

PERSONAGES

Too'-le the Evening Star, a Chief of the First People

He-le'-jah the Cougar or Mountain Lion, another Chief, and partner of *Too'-le*

Kah'-kool the Raven, who became a great hunter

To-lo'-mah the Bobcat

Yu'-wel the Gray Fox

How Kah-kool the Raven became a Great Hunter

A LONG time ago *Too'-le* the Evening Star lived at *Oo'-tin* [Bower Cave, on the Coulterville road to Yosemite]. *He-le'-jah* the Mountain Lion lived with him. They were chiefs and partners and had a room on the north side of the cave. There were other people here also — *To-lo'-mah* the Wild Cat, *Yu'-wel* the Gray Fox, *Kah'-kool* the Raven, and many more.

They used to send out hunters for meat. One of these, *Kah'-kool* the Raven, complained to *Too'-le* and *He-le'-jah* that he could not come near enough the game to shoot; the animals saw him too easily — he was too light colored. So he decided to make himself black; he took some charcoal and mashed it in a basket and rubbed it all over his body wherever he could reach, and had the others help put it on his back where he could not reach. When he was black all over he went hunting and killed two or three animals the first day, for now they could not see him.

One day *Kah'-kool* went to Big Meadows and climbed on top of Pile Peak, and when the moon rose, he saw away in the east two big things like ears standing up. He had never seen anything like

them before and ran back to *Oo'-tin* and told the
Chiefs. He said the animal must be very big and
very wild, for it turned its big ears every way. He
wanted to see it.

Every evening he went back to the peak and saw
the ears in the east, and each time they were a little
nearer. But he did not yet know what the animal
was. Then he went again and this time the ears
were only two or three miles away, and he ran
back quickly and told the Chiefs that the new animals were coming. They were Deer coming over
the mountains from the east; they had never been
here before.

The next morning *Kah'-kool* went out and for
the first time in his life saw a bunch of Deer; but
he did not know what they were. He saw that they
stepped quickly, and that some of them had horns.
So he ran back and told *Too'-le* and *He-le'-jah*
what he had seen, and said that the new animals
looked good to eat and he wanted to kill one.

"All right," answered the Chiefs, " If you see one
on our side [13] go ahead and kill him."

So the next morning *Kah'-kool* again went out
and saw that the animals had come much nearer
and were pretty close. He hid behind a tree and
they came still nearer. He picked out a big one
and shot his arrow into it and killed it, for he want-

---

[13] Meaning "on our side" of the tribal boundary line. This line
now separates the territory of the Middle Mewuk from that of the
Mono Lake Piutes.

Kah'-kool the Raven-hunter bringing in his first Deer. "*He-le'-jah* said it was a Deer and was good to eat."

ed to try the meat. He watched it kick and roll over and die, and then went back and told the Chiefs that he had killed one and wanted two men to go with him and fetch it. The Chiefs sent two men with him, but when they got there they had nothing to cut it with and had to carry it home whole. One took it by the front feet, the other by the hind feet; they carried it to the cave and showed it to the Chiefs.

He-le'-jah said it was a Deer and was good to eat, and told the people to skin it. They did so and ate it all at one meal.

Next morning *Kah'-kool* returned alone to the same place and followed the tracks and soon found the Deer. He hid behind a tree and shot one. The others ran, but he shot his arrows so quickly that they made only a few jumps before he had killed five—enough for all the people. He did not want to kill all; he wanted to leave some bucks and does so there would be more.

This time the Chiefs sent five men with *Kah'-kool*. They took flint knives and skinned the Deer and carried home all the meat and intestines for supper and breakfast.

Chief *Too'-le* the Evening Star told *Kah'-kool* that he wanted to see how the Deer walked, and would hunt with him. *Kah'-kool* replied that he was too light—too shiny—and would scare the Deer. *Too'-le* said he would hide behind a tree and not show himself. So he went, and *Kah'-kool* kept him

6

behind. But he was so bright that the Deer saw him and ran away. *Too'-le* said, "What am I going to do?" *Kah'-kool* made no answer; he was angry because he had to go home without any meat.

Next morning *Too'-le* went again. He said he was smart and knew what he would do. The Deer had now made a trail. *Too'-le* dug a hole by the trail and covered himself up with leaves and thought that when the Deer came he would catch one by the foot. But when the Deer came they saw his eye shine and ran away.

The next morning he tried again. He said that this time he would bury himself eye and all, and catch a Deer by the foot. *Kah'-kool* answered, "You can't catch one that way, you will have to shoot him." But *Too'-le* dug a hole in another place in the trail and covered himself all up, eye and all, except the tips of his fingers. The Deer came and saw the tips of his fingers shine and ran away. So again the hunters had to go back without any meat.

Then *Too'-le* the Evening Star said, "I'm going to black myself with charcoal, the same as *Kah'-kool* did." He tried, but the charcoal would not stick – he was too bright. He said, "I don't know what to do; I want to kill one or two Deer." Then he tried again and mashed more charcoal and put it on thick. The others helped him and finally made him black all over. *Too'-le* did not know that the Deer could smell him, and again hid on

98

the trail. The Deer came again. This time the
doe was ahead, the buck behind. The leader, the
doe, smelled him and jumped over him; the buck
smelled him and ran back. So this time also *Too'-
le* and *Kah'-kool* had to go home without meat.

The next morning *Too'-le* tried once more. He
had two men blacken him all over. Then he went
to the trail and stood still between two trees. But
the Deer smelled him and swung around and ran
away and went down west to the low country. This
discouraged him so that he did not know what to
do, and he gave up hunting and stayed at home.

Then *Kah'-kool* began to hunt again; he went
every morning alone and killed five or ten Deer.
The people ate the meat and intestines and all, but
did not have enough. Then *Kah'-kool* worked
harder; he started very early in the morning, before
daylight, and killed twelve to fifteen Deer every
day. This was too much for him and before long
he took sick and could not hunt at all.

Then the Chiefs and all the others had nothing
to eat and did not know what to do. *Too'-le* asked
He-le'-jah, and *He-le'-jah* asked *Too'-le*, what they
should do. *He-le'-jah* said he would stay and kill
his own Deer and eat the liver only – not the meat –
and would eat it raw. *Too'-le* said he would go up
into the sky and stay there and become the Evening
Star. And each did as he had said. So the rancheria at *Oo'-tin* was broken up.

How Kah'-kah-loo the Ravens became People

Fragment of a Tale of the Northern Mewuk

Personages

Kah'-kah-loo the Ravens
Me'-wuk the People

How Kah'-kah-loo the Ravens became People

WHEN water covered the world only the top of the highest mountain rose above it. The people had climbed up on this mountain, but could find no food and were starving. They wanted to go off and get something to eat. When the water went down all the ground was soft mud. After a while the people rolled rocks down to see if the mud were hard enough to hold them. When the rocks stayed on top, the people went down to search for food.

But the mud was not hard enough to hold them and they sank out of sight, leaving deep holes where they had gone down. Then *Kah'-kah-loo* the Ravens came and stood at the holes, one at each hole where a man had gone down. After a while, when the ground hardened, the Ravens turned into people. That is the reason the *Mewuk* are so dark.

THE BEAR AND THE FAWNS
As told by the Northern Mewuk in the Mokelumne River foothills

PERSONAGES

Oo-soo'-ma-te the Grizzly Bear-woman
O-woo'-yah the Mother Deer

102

The Bear and the Fawns

OO-SOO'-MA-TE the Grizzly Bear had a sister-in-law whose name was *O-woo'-yah* the Deer. *Oo-soo'-ma-te* took her to a place in the woods to show her a good kind of clover. When they found it *O-woo'-yah* began to scratch her head. *Oo-soo'-ma-te* said, "Let me look in your head," and seized her by the neck and killed her, and took her liver out and put it in a basket and carried it home.

O-woo'-yah the Deer was the mother of two little fawns, brothers, and *Oo-soo'-ma-te* was the mother of a little boy – a little bear cub.

When *Oo-soo'-ma-te* came home with the liver in her basket the little fawns asked, "Aunt, where is our mother?"

The Bear replied, "She is out gathering clover."

After a little they asked, "Why doesn't mother come home?" Then they saw the liver in the basket and smelled it and knew it was their mother's liver. Then they began to cry and say, "Our mother is dead, our mother is dead."

Old *Oo-soo'-ma-te* was outside pounding acorns. The little fawns went out and asked if they might take her baby and play with it.

She answered, "All right, but don't hurt him."

103

So they took the baby bear out in the woods to play, and went to the side of a hill and dug a hole. They said to the cub, "We will go in first and you close the hole and smoke us, and when we call, you let us out. Then you go in and we will smoke you."

So they went in first and the baby bear closed the hole and made smoke go in, and when the smoke was thick the fawns called to be let out, and the cub let them out. Then the cub went in and the fawns closed the hole and made smoke go in. The cub said, "When I call, you let me out," and the fawns answered, "All right." But when the bear cub called to be let out the fawns poked more leaves and pine needles into the hole and made more smoke, and the little bear kept crying till he died. After he was dead they took him out.

Then they said, "What shall we do? What shall we tell our Aunt?"

Just then *Oo-soo'-ma-te*, who was still pounding acorns, called them to come home.

The fawns laid the baby bear on the ground near the house so their Aunt could see it, and told her it was asleep and they were going to play again.

She answered, "Don't go far, your mother will be here pretty soon."

The little brothers then ran off to the south as fast as they could go, so *Oo-soo'-ma-te* could not find them. Every time they passed a tree on the

The Fawns asking Mother Bear if they may play with her Baby

trail they peeled a little bark off and spat on the place and told it to call out when *Oo-soo'-ma-te* came looking for them. This they did to all the trees till they came to a big river with a high hill on the far side; then they crossed the river and climbed up the hill.

Soon the trees began to shout and the fawns knew that *Oo-soo'-ma-te* was coming, and after a while they saw her coming. She saw them on the far side of the river and asked how they had crossed. They told her to turn her head the other way and walk backward. Then they quickly made a hot fire and heated two big rocks with hard white chunks in them.

When *Oo-soo'-ma-te* was nearly across the river the older fawn went to the edge of the water and knelt down, and the younger one rolled a hot rock, which just missed his brother's knee. The older one then ran up to the fire and said, " Let me do that and you kneel down." And he took the other big hot rock, and rolled it down the hill. It grazed his brother's knee a little and then hit the old bear and she fell back in the river and was drowned.

Then the fawns began to wonder what they had better do. First they dragged the old bear out of the water and cut her hide on the back and made a long rope of it and took the rope with them. Then the younger one asked, "Where are we going now? Up east?"

"No," answered the elder one.

"Where then, going north?"

"No."

"Going west?"

"No."

"Where then, south?"

"No."

"Then where are we going, up in the sky?" asked the little one.

"No," replied the other.

"Are we going under the earth?"

"Yes," said the elder brother.

Then the younger one said, "You don't know where we are going; ask me." And the elder brother asked the younger, "Are we going north?"

"No," was the reply.

"West?"

"No."

"South?"

"No."

"Where then, under the earth?"

"No."

"Where do you want to go – up in the sky?"

"Yes," answered the younger; so they went up in the sky and there they found their mother.

She was glad to see her boys. They said, "We are thirsty; where is the water?" She answered, "I have no water here, I'll go to the spring to get it." And she went to the spring and fell in and was drowned. Then the brothers let themselves down with the rope they had made from the hide of the Mother Bear, and came back to this world. If their mother had not drowned, the fawns would have stayed up there and there would be no deer here on the earth.

THE BEAR AND THE FAWNS
OUTLINE OF STORY SUNG BY THE MIDDLE MEWUK IN THE MOUNTAINS ON TUOLUMNE RIVER

PERSONAGES
Oo-soo'-ma-te the Grizzly Bear-woman
Ut-too'-yah the Mother Deer
He-le'-jah the Cougar or Mountain Lion-man
Te-wi'-yu the Red-shafted Flicker-man

110

The Bear and the Fawns

A story sung by the Middle Mewuk

OO-SOO'-MA-TE the Grizzly Bear killed *Ut-too'-yah* the Mother Deer. *Oo-soo'-ma-te* killed her and *He-le'-jah* the Mountain Lion ate her. The Mother Deer had two little fawns. They missed their mother and asked *Oo-soo'-ma-te* where she was. *Oo-soo'-ma-te* answered, "She is resting," and pointing to the house said, "Go in there where you will be safe till she comes back."

They went in, singing for their mother to come back, for they were starving. When they were inside, *Oo-soo'-ma-te* closed the door so they could not get out.

Then the fawns felt sure that *Oo-soo'-ma-te* had killed their mother and was intending to kill them. So they fastened the door of the Bear's house on the inside so she could not get in. Then a kind one—*Te-wi'-yu* the Red-shafted Flicker—brought them fire and they put it in the middle of the house and put on a number of rocks to heat.

When *Oo-soo'-ma-te* came home she was unable to get in and called to the fawns, saying, "I want to come in; where is the door?"

They answered, "Try the west side."

111

She tried, but could not find any door.

Then they called to her to try the north side, and she did so, but could not find it.

Then they told her to try the east side, and she did, with no better success; then the south side, with the same result.

This made *Oo-soo'-ma-te* very angry and she shouted, " If you don't open the door and let me in I'll come and eat you."

Then they told her to climb up on top and come in through the smoke hole, and to back down or she would fall and break her neck.

So she climbed up on top and began to back down through the smoke hole. But by this time the rocks were hot, and while she was trying to squeeze through the hole the fawns took the hot rocks and burned her to death.

How the Children of He-le'-jah Became People

Fragment of Creation Story of the Northern Mewuk
As told at *Wal'-le* and *Hä'-cha-nah*

PERSONAGES

He-le'-jah the Cougar or Mountain Lion-man
Oo-soo'-ma-te the Grizzly Bear-woman, wife of *He-le'-jah*
Paht'-ki-yu the Raccoon-woman, another wife of *He-le'-jah*
Pe-tä'-le the Little Lizard-man, who gave the people five
fingers

114

How the Children of He-le'-jah became People

HE-LE'-JAH the Cougar or Mountain Lion had two wives, *Oo-soo'-ma-te* the Grizzly Bear-woman and *Paht'-ki-yu* the Raccoon-woman. Their children looked a little like people but still were not people. Every year there were more children, and as they grew up and had children of their own, the children came to look more and more like people, only they had no fingers.

Then *Pe-tā'-le* the Lizard gave them five fingers and they became real people (*Me'wuk*).

7

THE GREED OF HIS'-SIK THE SKUNK

A TALE OF THE SOUTHERN MEWUK

As told by the Mariposa Mewuk

His'-sik the Skunk was Chief of a village or rancheria of the Foothills People at a place in the lower hills of Mariposa County nearly midway between Indian Gulch and Hornitos.

PERSONAGES

His'-sik the Skunk, a greedy chief of the Foothills People

Yu'-wel the Gray Fox, a hunter who married *His'-sik's* daughter

So'-koi the Elk

Too'-wik the Badger, who outwitted *His'-sik*

116

The Greed of His'-sik the Skunk

HIS'-SIK the Skunk had a wife, and by and by a daughter, who, when she grew up, married *Yu'-wel* the Gray Fox. *Yu'-wel* was a good hunter and he and *His'-sik* often hunted together.

Not far from *His'-sik's* place were two high hills standing side by side. In the narrow gap between them ran the trail of *So'-koi* the Elk. One day *His'-sik* told *Yu'-wel* to hide in this narrow place while he went down to the plain to drive up the elk. So *Yu'-wel* hid there and *His'-sik* went down near the elk and fired his terrible scent. The elk could not stand the smell and ran up the trail. *Yu'-wel* waited until the leader and all the others had passed up between the hills, and when the last one had gone by he stepped behind him and fired his arrow with such force that it shot through the whole band, killing them all.

When *His'-sik* came he was so glad that he danced. He called all the people to come and help carry the meat home; and then said to *Yu'-wel*: "You must pack one elk and pack me too, for I am too tired to walk."

Yu'-wel was afraid of *His'-sik* and so did as he was told. He lifted a big elk on his shoulders,

117

and *His'-sik* climbed up on top, and while they were on the way danced all the time on the body of the elk, and *Yu'-wel* carried them both to the village.

Then *His'-sik* told the people to skin the elk, and promised them some of the meat. They skinned the elk and cut the meat in strips and hung it up to dry. When they had done this they asked him for their share. He refused to give them any but told them that they might eat acorn mush and pinole. He then turned as if he were going to shoot his scent, and everyone was afraid.

His'-sik was so greedy that he would not give any of the meat to anyone – not even to his own wife and daughter, nor to his son-in-law who killed it – but put it all away to dry for himself.

The next day he told *Yu'-wel* to hunt again, and they did the same as before; and when the elk were in the narrow pass between the hills *Yu'-wel* shot his arrow and killed the whole bunch, as before.

Then *His'-sik* called the people to come and carry the elk home, and made *Yu'-wel* carry one, and he danced on top on the way, as before.

Again he told the people to skin the elk and he would give them meat for supper; but when they had skinned the elk and cut up the meat he told them to eat acorns and pinole, at the same time turning to frighten them, and took all the meat to dry for himself, just as he had done before.

118

The people were very angry, but were afraid to do anything for fear *His'-sik* would shoot his scent and kill them. They talked the matter over for a long time and finally a wise man said: "What are we going to do? Must we hunt for him and pack his meat and skin it for him always, and not get any? We had better kill him, but how can we do it so he will not shoot his scent and kill us?"

Then *Too'-wik* the Badger spoke. He said, "We can kill him." And while *His'-sik* was watching his meat so no one could take any of it, *Too'-wik* dug a big hole, ten or fifteen feet deep, and built a fire in it.

Someone asked him why he made the fire. *Too'-wik* replied, "Do you not know that *His'-sik* is a great dancer and loves to dance? We will have fire in the hole, and cover the top over with sticks and leaves and earth so he can't see anything, and send for him to come and dance, and when he dances he will break through and fall in and we shall kill him."

The people answered, "All right."

When it was dark they sent a messenger to *His'-sik*. He said, "You are a great dancer; we want a dance tonight and will pay you well if you will come."

His'-sik was pleased and answered, "All right, where shall I dance?"

They took him to the place and pointing to it said, "Right here."

His'-sik began to dance and sing, and everyone said, "Good, you are doing well; keep on, you are doing finely; go ahead, you surely are a great dancer." And they flattered him and he kept on and danced harder and harder, for he was proud and wanted to show what he could do.

After a while, when he was dancing hardest, the sticks broke and he fell into the hole. The people were ready. They had a big rock, a very big rock, which it had taken many people to bring. They were waiting, and the moment he fell in they pushed the rock quickly over the hole and held it down; they all climbed up on it and held it down tight so he could not get out.

The hot coals burnt his feet and made him dance. He was very angry and shot his scent so hard against the side of the hole that he pushed mountains up on that side; then he turned the other way and shot again and pushed mountains up on that side too. After this his scent was gone and the coals burnt him and killed him. Then all the people were happy.

The next day the people had a great feast and ate all the dried meat they wanted.

NEK'-NA-KA'-TAH THE ROCK MAIDEN
A Tale of the Northern Mewuk
As told at *Wal'-le* near the Canyon of Mokelumne River

PERSONAGES
Nek'-na-kā'-tah the Rock Maiden
Oo-soo'-ma-te the Grizzly Bear

122

Ancient Mortar-holes in the Granite Rock

Nek'-na-ka'-tah the Rock Maiden

IN the mountains among the rocks by the river lives *Nek'-na-kā'-tah*, the little rock girl. She is herself a rock and always lives in rocky places by the river. In some way she produces or gives off people; these people are hard like rocks and you can not cut them or shoot them with an arrow.

A long time ago *Oo-soo'-ma-te* the Grizzly Bear and *Hoi-yah'-ko* the FIRST PEOPLE, made the *Chaw'-se* or mortar holes in the big flat-topped rocks. Then *Nek'-na-kā'-tah* the rock maiden came and helped make the *Kah-wah'-che* or stone pestles for the people to pound acorns with.

125

The Jealousy of Wek'-wek and the Death of Lo'-wut

A Tale of the Wĭ'-pa Tribe

The Wĭ'-pä lived on No'-yoop Island between the Sacramento and San Joaquin Rivers, east of Suisun Bay. They are now extinct. The last survivor, an old woman named *E'-non-na-too-yä*, to whom the author is indebted for the following remarkable story, died during the winter of 1908-1909.

Personages

O-lā'-nah the Coyote-man
Wek'-wek the Falcon, Chief of the Bird People
Ho'-pah the White-headed Eagle
Lo'-wut the Gray Goose, wife of *Wek'-wek*
To-to'-kol the Sandhill Crane, mother of *Lo'-wut*
Soo'-choo-koo the Spoon-bill Duck
Yu-koo'-le the Meadowlark

The Jealousy of Wek'-wek and the Death of Lo'-wut

WEK'-WEK the Falcon-man was Chief and Captain of all the bird-people. He used to hunt birds for food and also used to catch birds alive to bring back to his *han-nā'-boo* (roundhouse) where he kept them locked up until he could turn them into people. *O-lā'-nah* the Coyote-man stood guard at the door of the *han-nā'-boo*.

Wek'-wek the Falcon-man and *Ho'-pah* the White-headed Eagle-man had the power to make people out of birds. For this reason they were jealous of one another. Besides, *Ho'-pah* was in love with *Wek'-wek's* wife, *Lo'-wut*, the Gray Goose-woman. So *Wek'-wek* had cause to be jealous.

Once when he went out to go hunting he hid and watched and saw *Ho'-pah* and *Lo'-wut* together. This made him very angry. When he came back he asked *Lo'-wut*, his wife, "Have you anything ready to eat? I'm hungry."

"Yes," she replied.

"Bring me some water first," he said, "I'm thirsty; bring good water; don't get it from the

127

edge of the river; go out where it is deep and get it there."

Lo'-wut did as she was told and came back with good clear water, but when she reached the house with it, it had turned into snakes and frogs and other water animals. [14] Five times she went out into the river for water, each time with the same result. The last time she waded out till the water was above her waist.

While she was gone, *Wek'-wek* went to her bed and fixed in it four long spear points of flint with the points up. When she came the fifth time with snakes and frogs instead of water, *Wek'-wek* seized her and threw her down on the bed and the four spear points pierced her body and killed her.

To-to'-kol the Sandhill Crane-woman was *Lo'-wut's* mother; she was very angry because *Wek'-wek* had killed her daughter, and wanted to punish him.

O-lā'-nah the Coyote-man and *Soo'-choo-koo* the Spoon-bill Duck came to carry *Lo'-wut's* dead body to the *han-nā'-boo*, but when they lifted it they saw on the breast the black marks which *Ho'-pah* her lover had painted there. *Wek'-wek* had seen these before and knew. So *O-lā'-nah* and *Soo'-choo-koo* took the dead body and buried it.

When *Lo'-wut* died she left two children, a baby and a little boy. Their grandmother, *To-to'-kol*,

---

14 *Wek'-wek* made this happen, for he was a magician or witch doctor.

Funeral of *Lo'-wut*, wife of *Wek'-wek*

took care of them and every day sent the little boy with the baby to the roundhouse to be fed – and for four days *Lo'-wut* the dead mother came each day to the *han-nā'-boo* to give milk to her young child.

On the fourth day *Wek'-wek* asked his little boy where he went every day with the little one. The boy, afraid to tell the truth, said he took the child to give it milk of the milkweed plant.

Wek'-wek hid in the top of an oak tree and watched. He saw his dead wife *Lo'-wut* come to the roundhouse to give breast to the child; and saw her rise from the ground and shake the earth of the grave out of her hair.

Then *Wek'-wek* found that he loved her still, although she had been unfaithful to him. So he went into the roundhouse and caught her in his arms and hugged her.

"Let me go," she said, "You can't get me back; I'm not well as I used to be."

"That doesn't make any difference," he said, "I'll cure you." And he took her away to his own roundhouse, where the other bird-people were. It was dark when they arrived.

Yu-koo'-le the Meadowlark was there. He had never liked *Wek'-wek's* wife and had quarrelled with her. Now he made a great fuss and noise.

"*Hoo*," he said, "light a light; I smell something like a dead body."

At that very moment *Wek'-wek* was sitting in the

middle of the roundhouse holding the body of his wife, whom he was bringing back to life. But when *Yu-koo'-le* spoke and said what he did, the dead woman disappeared.

Wek'-wek was very angry. He spoke and said to the rest of the birds (all of whom were going to be people) : "This now is the way it will be with us all. When we die we shall die forever. Had it not been for *Yu-koo'-le* we would live again after the fourth day and be alive forever, the same as before."

When *Wek'-wek* had said this he seized *Yu-koo'-le* and tore his mouth open and killed him, and to this day you can see under the meadowlark's throat the black mark where his mouth was torn down, and the marks on his head where the skull was crushed.

Then *Wek'-wek* sent all the bird-people away, but before they went he spoke to them and said: "Now you will never be people but will be real birds; if *Yu-koo'-le* had not said what he did my wife would have lived and all of you would have turned into people."

All the bird-people in the roundhouse were angry at what *Yu-koo'-le* had done. They said, "Were it not for *Yu-koo'-le* we would turn into people; now we must turn into animals." Then they came out of the roundhouse, one at a time, and as each came out it sang the song of the kind of bird it was to be, and became that kind, and went away.

132

The Defeat of O-la'-nah the Coyote-Man
Fragment of a Tale of the Wi'pa Tribe

PERSONAGES
O-lā'-nah the Coyote-man
Wek'-wek the Falcon
O-hul'-le the Badger, wife of *O-lā'-nah*

The Defeat of O-la′-nah the Coyote-man

WEK′-WEK the Falcon-man and *O-lā′-nah* the Coyote-man lived a long time ago.

Wek′-wek did not like *O-lā′-nah* because he was smart and always pretended that he could do everything. So one day *Wek′-wek* said to him, "Let's go and get wood; you are so smart and know so much and can do so many things, let's see you take that big oak tree and bring it home."

O-lā′-nah answered, "All right, I can do it."

Wek′-wek told him to go ahead and do it.

Then *O-lā′-nah* ran around and around the big oak tree and the roots cracked and made a noise, and the tree shook, but it did not fall; *O-lā′-nah* could not get it up; he made it shake four times but could not make it fall.

Wek′-wek, who was watching from the top of a sycamore tree, said, "Do that again; make the big oak tree shake again, the same as you did before, you are so strong."

O-lā′-nah tried but could not do it.

Then *Wek′-wek* said: "What you said was not true; you bragged that you could do everything but you can not do any thing; now I have beaten you, haven't I?"

"Yes," answered *O-lā'-nah*, "You have beaten me; I am going away." Then *O-lā'-nah* turned and howled as Coyotes howl and cried and said "*how-loo'-loo-e, how-loo'-loo-e, how-loo'-loo-e,*" and turned into a real Coyote like the coyotes we have now. But he was angry and set upon *O-hul'-le*, his wife (*O-hul'-le* was the Badger-woman), and whipped her, and she ran away. *O-lā'-nah* followed and tried to bring her back, but she refused and would not come.

After *Wek'-wek* had beaten *O-lā'-nah* he had to get fire. So he went up the Sacramento River to the place where trees grow, where the creeks come down from the mountains, and took a piece of wood and made a small hole in it and sprinkled in the hole some dry leaves of *Kutch'-um* the sage-herb, and took a stick of *Lap'-pah*, the elderberry tree, and whirled it between his hands, with one end in the hole in the wood, and fire came in the dry *Kutch'-um* leaves and he had fire.

How Sah'-te Set the World on Fire

A Tale of the Tu'-le-yo-me Tribe

Among the low hills about four miles south of Clear Lake is the site of an ancient Indian settlement named *Tu'-le-yo'-me poo-koot*. It was the ancestral home of the *Tu'-le-yo'-me* or *O'-lā-yo-me* tribe, the last vanishing remnant of which is now located on Putah Creek a few miles east of Middletown.

PERSONAGES

Ol'-le the Coyote-man

Wek'-wek the Falcon, grandson of *Ol'-le*

Hoo-yu'-mah the Meadowlark

Lah'-kah the Canada Goose

Sah'-te the Weasel-man, who set the world on fire

Hoo-poos'-min brothers, two small Grebes or Hell-divers (*Podilymbus podiceps*)

We'-ke-wil'-lah brothers, two little Shrews (*Sorex*) who stole the fire

Kah'-kah-te the Crow, whose fire was stolen by the *We'-ke-wil'-lah* brothers

How Sah-te set the World on Fire

ALONG time ago, before there were any Indian people, *Ol'-le* the Coyote-man and his grandson, *Wek'-wek* the Falcon, lived together at *Tu'-le-yo'-me*. In those days *Wek'-wek* hunted *Hoo-yu'-mah* the Meadowlark and ate no other game, and *Ol'-le* the Coyote-man ate nothing at all.

One day *Wek'-wek* said: "Grandfather, I want to see what is on the other side of *Mel'-le-a-loo'-mah*.[15] I want to see the country on the other side."

"All right," answered *Ol'-le*.

So the next morning *Wek'-wek* set out and crossed over the *Mel'-le-a-loo'-mah* hills to Coyote Valley, and a little farther on came to a small lake called *Wen'-nok pol'-pol*, at the south end of which was a pretty pointed mountain called *Loo-peek'-pow-we*. On the lake were great numbers of ducks and geese. Up to this time he had never killed any of these – he had killed only *Hoo-yu'-mah* the Meadowlark.

He went back to *Tu'-le-yo'-me*, and told his grandfather what he had seen, and asked how he

---

15 *Mel'-le-a-loo'-mah* is the name of the hill-country south of Lower Lake – between Lower Lake and Coyote Valley.

139

could get the ducks and geese. His grandfather answered: "A long time ago my father taught me how to make *low'-ke* the sling, and how to put *loo'-poo* the small stone in it, and how to aim and fire by swinging it around and letting fly." Then *Ol'-le* took *kol* the tule and made a *low'-ke* of it for *Wek'-wek*. The next morning *Wek'-wek* took the *low'-ke* and *loo'-poo* and went back to *Wen'-nok pol'-pol,* the little lake, and stood on top of *Loo-peek'-pow-we* the sharp-pointed mountain at the south end of the lake, from which he could see over all the valley. The flat ground at the base of the mountain was covered with geese of the black-neck kind called *Lah'-kah.* At the foot of the peak was a small flat-topped blue oak tree, the kind called *moo-le.*[16] When the geese, which were walking on the ground, came up to this tree, *Wek'-wek* took careful aim with his *low'-ke* and let fly and the stone flew down among them and killed more than two hundred, and then came back to his hand. He at once fired again and killed several hundred more. He then gathered them all and packed them on his head back to *Tu'-le-yo'-me* and gave them to his grandfather, *Ol'-le* the Coyote-man.

Next morning when *Wek'-wek* was sitting on top of the roundhouse he saw someone coming. It was *Sah'-te* the Weasel-man, who lives under the

---

[16] My informant pointed out this little old tree to me and said that when he was a little boy his father told him that it had always been there, just as it was in the days of *Wek'-wek.*

Ol'-le the Coyote-man and *Wek'-wek* the Falcon-man at their Roundhouse

ground; he passed on to the south without stopping. *Wek'-wek* said, "This looks like a man. Who is this man? Tomorrow morning I'll go and see." So next morning he went out again and sat on top of the roundhouse. Soon he saw *Sah'-te* coming; he came from the north and went off to the south. Then *Wek'-wek* also went south; he went to the sharp peak, *Loo-peek'-pow'-we,* and saw *Sah'-te* pass and go still farther south.

Wek'-wek returned to *Tu'-le-yo'-me* and presently saw *Sah'-te* come and go north again toward Clear Lake. *Wek'-wek* wanted to find out where *Sah'-te* lived, so he went up to Clear Lake and at the head of Sulphurbank Bay he found *Sah'-te's lah'-mah* (roundhouse). He said to himself, "Now I've got you," and went into *Sah'-te's* house. But *Sah'-te* was not at home. *Wek'-wek* looked around and saw a great quantity of *hoo'-yah*, the shell beads or money. It was in skin sacks. He took these sacks – ten or twelve of them – and emptied the shell money out on a bear skin robe and packed it on his head back to *Tu'-le-yo'-me*. But he did not take it in to show his grandfather; he hid it in a small creek near by and did not say anything about it.

When *Sah'-te* came home he found that his beads were gone. "Who stole my beads?" he asked.

He then took his *yah'-tse* [the stick the people used to wear crossways in a twist of their back hair] and stood it up in the fire, and *oo'-loop* the flame climbed it and stood on the top. He then

143

took the *yah'-tse* with the flame at one end and said
he would find out who stole his shell money. First
he pointed it to the north, but nothing happened;
then to the west, and nothing happened; then east;
then up; then down, and still nothing happened.
Then he pointed it south toward *Tu'-le-yo'-me* and
the flame leaped from the stick and spread swiftly
down the east side of Lower Lake, burning the
grass and brush and making a great smoke.

In the evening *Wek'-wek* came out of the roundhouse at *Tu'-le-yo'-me* and saw the country to the
north on fire. He went in and told his grandfather that something was burning on Clear Lake.

Ol'-le the Coyote-man answered, "That's nothing; the people up there are burning tules."

Ol'-le knew what *Wek'-wek* had done, and knew
that *Sah'-te* had sent the fire, for *Ol'-le* was a magician and knew everything, but he did not tell
Wek'-wek that he knew.

After a while *Wek'-wek* came out again and
looked at the fire and saw that it was much nearer
and was coming on swiftly. He was afraid, and
went back and told his grandfather that the fire
was too near and too hot and would soon reach
them. After a little he went out again and came
back and said, "Grandfather, the fire is coming
fast; it is on this side of the lake and is awfully
hot."

Ol'-le answered, "That's nothing; the people
at Lower Lake are burning tules."

But now the roar and heat of the fire were terrible, even inside the roundhouse, and *Wek'-wek* thought they would soon burn. He was so badly frightened that he told his grandfather what he had done. He said, "Grandfather, I stole *Sah'-te's hoo'-yah* and put it in the creek, and now I'm afraid we shall burn."

Then *Ol'-le* took a sack and came out of the roundhouse and struck the sack against an oak tree, and fog came out. He struck the tree several times and each time more fog came out and spread around.

Then he went back in the house and got another sack and beat the tree, and more fog came, and then rain. He said to *Wek'-wek*, "It is going to rain for ten days and ten nights." And it did rain, and the rain covered the whole country till all the land and all the hills and all the mountains were under water—everything except the top of *Oo-de'-pow-we* (Mount Konokti, on the west side of Clear Lake) which was so high that its top stuck out a little.

There was no place for *Wek'-wek* to go and he flew about in the rain till he was all tired out. Finally he found the top of *Oo-de'-pow-we* and sat down on it and stayed there.

On the tenth day the rain stopped, and after that the water began to go down and each day the mountain stood up higher. *Wek'-wek* stayed on the mountain about a week, by which time the water had gone down and the land was bare again.

In Clear Lake near *Oo-de'-pow-we* is an island which was the home of two small grebes, diving birds, called *Hoo-poos'-min*. They were brothers and had a roundhouse, and in the roundhouse a fire. *Wek'-wek* went there and stayed two or three days, and then said he was going back to *Tu'-le-yo'-me*.

"All right," answered the *Hoo-poos'-min* brothers, "but don't tell *Ol'-le* that we have fire."

"All right," answered *Wek'-wek*, and he went off to *Tu'-le-yo'-me* to see *Ol'-le*, his grandfather.

When *Wek'-wek* arrived *Ol'-le* asked: "Who are you? I'm *Ol'-le*, and I live at *Tu'-le-yo'-me*."

Wek'-wek answered, "I'm *Wek'-wek* and I also live at *Tu'-le-yo'-me*."

"Oh yes," said *Ol'-le,* "you are *Hoi'-poo* (Captain) *Wek'-wek*."

"Yes," answered *Wek'-wek*.

At that time there were no real people in the world and *Wek'-wek* said, "There are no people; I'm lonesome; what are we going to do?"

Then *Ol'-le* told *Wek'-wek* to bring the feathers of the geese he had killed at *Wen'-nok* Lake. *Wek'-wek* did so, and they set out and traveled over the country. Wherever they found a good place for people *Ol'-le* took two feathers and laid them down side by side on the ground – two together side by side in one place, two together side by side in another place, and so on in each place

Wek'-wek on the hilltop killing Geese with his Sling

where he wanted a rancheria; and at the same time he gave each place its name.

Next morning they again went out and found that all the feathers had turned into people; that each pair of feathers had become two people, a man and a woman, so that at each place there were a man and a woman. This is the way all the rancherias were started.

By and by all the people had children and after a while the people became very numerous.

Wek'-wek was pleased and said, "This is good." A little later he asked, "Grandfather, now that we have people, what are we going to do? There is no fire; what can we do to get fire?"

Ol'-le replied, " I don't know; we shall see pretty soon."

Ol'-le had a small box in his roundhouse and in it kept two little Shrew-mice of the kind called *We'-ke-wil'-lah*. They were brothers. *Ol'-le* said to them: "*Kah'-kah-te* the Crow has fire in his roundhouse, far away in the east; you go and steal it."

We'-ke-wil'-lah the little Shrew-mice said they would try, and set out on their long journey and went far away to the east and finally came to *Kah'-kah-te's* roundhouse. They heard *Kah'-kah-te* say, "*kah'-ahk*," and saw a spark of fire come out of the hole on top of the house. Then they went to a dead tree and got some *too-koom'* (the kind of buckskin that comes on dead wood) and cut off a

149

piece and took it and climbed up on top of
Kah'-kah-te's house and sat by the smoke hole and
waited. After a while *Kah'-kah-te* again said
"*kah'-ahk*," and another spark came out, but they
could not reach it. But the next time *Kah'-kah-te*
said "*kah'-ahk*" and another spark came out the
little brothers caught it in their *too-koom'*, the
wood buckskin.

When they had done this they caught a little bug
and pushed him in backward till he touched the
spark. Then they said, "Let's go," and set out at
once and traveled as fast as they could toward *Tu'-
le-yo'-me*.

Just then *Kah'-kah-te* the Crow came out of his
house and in the darkness saw a little speck of light
moving back and forth among the trees. It was
the fire bug going home with the little Shrew
brothers. *Kah'-kah-te* when he saw it cried, "Somebody has stolen my fire," and set out in pursuit.

The little brothers and the firefly were badly
frightened and ran around a little hill so *Kah'-kah-
te* could not see them, and hid under the bank of a
dry creek. *Kah'-kah-te* hunted for them for some
time but could not find them and went back to his
house. His mate, who was inside, said, "Nobody
stole our fire."

Kah'-kah-te answered, "Yes, someone stole it,
I saw it go around." Then he went back into his
house.

Then the *We'-ke-wil'-lah* brothers ran as fast

as they could all the way back to *Tu'-le-yo'-me* and arrived there the same night. They said to *Ol'-le*, "Grandfather, look," and tossed him the *too-koom'* – the tree buckskin with the fire inside. He unrolled it and found the fire and took it out and made a fire on the ground.

Wek'-wek exclaimed, "That is good; I'm glad; now everybody can have fire."

Then *Ol'-le* put the fire in the *oo'-noo* (buckeye) tree, and told the people how to rub the *oo'-noo* stick to make it come out. From that time to this everybody has known how to get fire from the *oo'-noo* tree.

How Cha'-ka the Tule-wren Shot Out the Sun

A Tale of the Olamentko Indians of Bodega Bay

Personages

O'-ye the Coyote-man
Chā'-kā the Tule-wren, a poor orphan boy
Koo-loo'-pe the Humming-bird

152

How Cha-ka the Tule-wren shot out the Sun

CHA'-KA the Tule-wren was a poor worthless boy. He had no father and no mother and went from house to house begging, and the people gave him food to eat. Nobody liked him, and finally they tired of feeding him. One day he told them that if they did not give him food he would shoot out the Sun. Then everybody laughed. Again he said he surely would shoot it out. They said, "Go ahead and shoot."

So he did; he sent his arrow right up into the Sun and let the light out and the whole world became dark. There was no Sun, no Moon, no Stars, no Fire – everything was dark. It was dark for years and years and the people could not see to find food, and everybody was starving.

All this time *O'-ye* the Coyote-man was thinking how he could get the Sun and light back again. At length he saw just a little light a long way off. He sent *Koo-loo'-pe* the Humming-bird to steal it.

Koo-loo'-pe set out on the long journey and finally came to the fire and stole a little piece and brought it back under his chin – you can see the blaze there to this day.

When he was bringing it somebody chased him, but he was so small and flew so swiftly they could not see which way he went and could not catch him. So he escaped with the fire and brought it back to *O'-ye* the Coyote-man, and the people had light again.

How Wek'-wek Was Saved from the Flood

Fragment of a Tale of the Olamentko Tribe of Bodega Bay

PERSONAGES

O'-ye the Coyote-man
Wek'-wek the Falcon
Pe'-leet the Grebe

156

How Wek'-wek was saved from the Flood

O'-YE the Coyote-man, and *Wek'-wek* the Falcon-man quarrelled. Then *O'-ye* gathered up the people and took them away with him across the ocean, leaving *Wek'-wek* alone. Then he made the rain come and cover the world with water. The water grew deeper and deeper and covered all the trees and all the hills and all the mountains until nothing was left but water.

Wek'-wek could find no place to rest—nothing to stand on—and had to fly and fly and fly till he was all tired out. By and by he could fly no longer and fell on the water and was floating around nearly dead when his wing caught on a little stick. This stick stuck up from the top of the roundhouse of *Pe'-leet* the Grebe, who came up to see what was the matter. He found *Wek'-wek* (a relative of his) nearly drowned and pulled him down into his roundhouse and saved him.

Then *O'-ye* the Coyote-man let the water down and brought the people back.

WHY THE BODEGA BAY INDIANS CAN NOT STAND COLD

A TALE OF THE BODEGA OLAMENTKO

PERSONAGE

O'-ye the Coyote-man

Why the Bodega Bay Indians can not stand Cold

WHEN *O'-ye* the Coyote-man had everything ready he thought he would make
people. So he gathered a lot of sticks of
different kinds – some hard, as oak, madrone, and
manzanita; some soft and hollow, as the sage-herb –
and made a big pile of them and said that by and by
they would turn into people.

Then he went over all the country and where-
ever he wanted a village he laid down two sticks,
and gave the place a name – and the name he gave
it then has always been its name and is its name to
this day. Then he went away.

In a short time the sticks turned into people,
and all the rancherias were started with the first
real people.

In places where he had put sticks of hard wood
the people were strong and well and warm-blooded
and could stand cold weather; but in places where
he put poor wood the people were weak and sickly
and could not stand cold weather. Here at Bodega Bay he left only sticks of *Po'-to-po'-to* the sage-
herb, [17] which has a hollow stem and has no strength.
That is the reason our people are tender and weak

---

[17] The sage-herb is a form of *Artemisia ludoviciana*.

159

and can not stand cold, and why nearly all died soon after the white men came. We are hollow inside and can not stand cold.

HOI-AH'-KO TALES OF THE SOUTHERN MEWUK

As told in the foothills of the Merced River region

THE TALES

Yel'-lo-kin and *Oo-wel'-lin* the man-eating Giants
Oo-wel'-lin the Rock Giant
Tim-me-lā'-le the Thunder
Wek'-wek's search for his Father
Wek'-wek's search for his Sister
Wek'-wek's visit to the Underworld

PRINCIPAL PERSONAGES

Hoi-ah'-ko the First People
We'-pi-ahk the Golden Eagle, Chief of the First People
Tu'-pe the Kangaroo-rat, *We'-pi-ahk's* wife
Yel'-lo-kin the Giant Bird who lived on top of the sky
Oo-wel'-lin the Rock Giant
Ol-lusmuk-ki'-e the Toad-woman, *We'-pi-ahk's* Aunt
Ah-hā'-le the Coyote-man
Oo'-choom the Fly
Tim-me-lā'-le the Thunder
Wek'-wek the Falcon
Yi'-yil, *Wek'-wek's* father
Yow'-hah the Mallard Duck, *Wek'-wek's* wife
Hoo-loo'-e the Dove, *Wek'-wek's* partner
O-wah'-to the big-headed Fire Lizard
Ho'-ho the Turkey Buzzard, a wicked Chief of the South
  People
Koo'-choo, another wicked Chief of the South People
Lol'-luk the Woodrat, one of the firemen
No-put'-kul-lol the Screech-owl, the other fireman
Pel-pel'-nah the Nuthatch, one of the witch doctors
Choo-ta-tok'-kwe-lah the Red-headed Sapsucker, the other
  witch doctor
Ah'-ut the Crow, *Wek'-wek's* nephew
O-hum'-mah-te the Grizzly Bear
He-le'-jah the Mountain Lion
To-to'-kon the Sandhill Crane, chief of the Underworld
  People

162

Hoi=ah=ko Tales of the Southern Mewuk

YEL'-LO-KIN AND OO-WEL'-LIN, THE MAN-EATING GIANTS

WE'-PI-AHK the Eagle was chief of the First People. He took for his wife *Tu'-pe* the Kangaroo-rat. She did not stay at home nights because night was the time she went out to hunt for food. *We'-pi-ahk* did not understand this and when she came back one morning he beat her and killed her. After that he stayed at home a month and cried and never went out. When the month was up he stopped crying and went out in the sun.

Next day *Yel'-lo-kin* came. *Yel'-lo-kin* was a giant bird – the biggest bird in the world. He was in the habit of carrying off children – boys and girls up to fourteen or fifteen years of age. He took them by the top of the head and carried them up through the hole in the middle of the sky to his home on top of the sky, where he killed and ate them.

Yel'-lo-kin had a wife. She was *Ol'-lus muk-ki'-e* the Toad-woman, the aunt of *We'-pi-ahk* the Eagle. *Yel'-lo-kin* had stolen her from the earth and had taken her up to his house above the sky.

163

He did not kill her but kept her as his wife, and brought people to her to eat; but she would not eat people.

When *We'-pi-ahk* the Eagle had gone out in the sun *Yel'-lo-kin* came and caught him by the top of his head and carried him up through the hole in the sky.

A boy playing outside saw this and shouted to the people, and they all got poles and bows and arrows and tried to reach *Yel'-lo-kin* but could not, and *Yel'-lo-kin* went on up with *We'-pi-ahk* and took him to his house on top of the sky and left him there. When *We'-pi-ahk* looked around he saw his aunt, *Ol'-lus muk-ki'-e* the Toad-woman. She told him to look out, that in a little while *Yel'-lo-kin* would come back and kill him. "He will take you to a big tank of blood and ask if you want to drink," she said. "When he does this you must answer 'yes' and pretend to reach down, and tell him the water is too low, you can't reach it; you are afraid of falling in. Ask him to show you how to get it."

"All right," answered *We'-pi-ahk* – he would do as she said.

Then she gave him a big stone knife with which to cut off *Yel'-lo-kin's* head.

Soon *Yel'-lo-kin* returned and did exactly as his wife said he would do. When he asked *We'-pi-ahk* to drink, *We'-pi-ahk* told him he could not reach the water; he was afraid of falling in, and asked *Yel'-lo-kin* to show him how. Then *Yel'-lo-kin* leaned over and reached down deep in the tank, and *We'-pi-ahk* struck him with the big knife and cut off his head, whereupon *Yel'-lo-kin* banged around inside the tank and flapped his big wings and made a great noise, and finally flopped out and died outside. He stretched out his wings and they were as big as pine trees. Then *We'-pi-ahk* was free.

Ah-hā'-le the Coyote-man was down below. *We'-pi-ahk* the Eagle was his uncle. *Ah-hā'-le* asked the people, "Where is my uncle, *We'-pi-ahk*?"

The boys told him he had gone up – that *Yel'-lo-kin* had carried him up through the sky. *Ah-hā'-le* looked but could not see the hole they had gone through. Then he went south and looked for the south hole in the sky, but could not find it. Returning, he went north to the hole at Thunder Mountain, but could not get in that way for it was too cold. Then he came back to the village and sprang up high in the air and passed through the middle hole in the sky – the same hole that *Yel'-lo-kin* had gone through with *We'-pi-ahk*.

Just as he arrived, at that very moment *We'-pi-ahk* struck *Yel'-lo-kin* with the knife and killed him, and *Ah-hā'-le* saw him die.

"It is a good thing that you killed him," *Ah-hā'-le* said.

We'-pi-ahk replied, "He has been stealing our boys and girls; whenever he was hungry he went down and got a boy or a girl. We lost lots of people."

Then *We'-pi-ahk* showed *Ah-hā'-le* the tank of blood where *Yel'-lo-kin* had done his killing.

After a while *Ah-hā'-le* asked, "What are you going to do with *Yel'-lo-kin?*"

We'-pi-ahk said he was going to burn him, so he would not come to life again.

But *Ah-hā'-le* replied, "No uncle, you had better not burn him."

Then *We'-pi-ahk* asked, "What are you going to do with him?"

Ah-hā'-le answered, "I think I'll cut off his wings and take them down home."

"What are you going to do with them?" asked *We'-pi-ahk.*

Ah-hā'-le replied, "I'm going to plant the big feathers and make trees. If I plant plenty of trees and everything green, there will be many people, for when I'm done planting trees I'm going to make people."

When he had finished speaking he went down to the earth through a hole of his own, for he was a witch doctor.

After he had gone down, *Yel'-lo-kin's* wife, *Ol'-lus muk-ki͏̈'-e* the Toad-woman, asked *We'-pi-ahk* how he was going to get down.

"I don't know," answered *We'-pi-ahk.*

"I'll take you down," said *Ol'-lus muk-ki͏̈'-e.*

"How," asked *We'-pi-ahk.*

"You will see how," she replied. And she gathered the strong green sword-grass called *kis'-soo*, that grows by the river, and made a long rope of it and with it let *We'-pi-ahk* down to the earth.

Ah-hă'-le the Coyote-man planted the feathers, and when they had come up watched them grow. They grew into grasses, wild oats, flowers, manzanitas, and other bushes, and into yellow pines, sugar pines, black oaks, blue oaks, and other kinds of trees. He told them all to bear seed every year so the people who were coming would have plenty to eat. He also made rivers and rocks — *Yel'-lo-kin's* heart he turned into a black rock.

When he had done this he made people. These also he made by planting feathers. The people multiplied and in a short time their villages were everywhere in the land.

Oo-wel'-lin the Rock Giant

THERE was a great Giant who lived in the north. His name was *Oo-wel'-lin*, and he was as big as a pine tree. When he saw the country full of people he said they looked good to eat, and came and carried them off and ate them. He could catch ten men at a time and hold them between his fingers, and put more in a net on his back, and carry them off. He would visit a village and after eating all the people would move on to another, going southward from his home in the north. When he had gone to the south end of the world and had visited all the villages and eaten nearly all the people—not quite all, for a few had escaped—he turned back toward the north. He crossed the *Wah-kal'-mut-ta* (Merced River) at a narrow place in the canyon about six miles above *Op'-lah* (Merced Falls) where his huge footprints may still be seen in the rocks, showing the exact place where he stepped from *Ang-e'-sa-wā'-pah* on the south side to *Hik-kā'-nah* on the north side. When night came he went into a cave in the side of a round-topped hill over the ridge from *Se-saw-che* [a little south of the present town of Coulter-ville].

The people who had escaped found his sleeping

169

place in the cave and shot their arrows at him but were not able to hurt him, for he was a rock giant.

When he awoke he was hungry and took the trail to go hunting. Then the people said to *Oo'-choom* the Fly: "Go follow *Oo-wel'-lin* and when he is hot bite him all over, on his head, on his eyes and ears, and all over his body, everywhere, all the way down to the bottoms of his feet, and find out where he can be hurt.

"All right," answered *Oo'-choom* the Fly, and he did as he was told. He followed *Oo-wel'-lin* and bit him everywhere from the top of his head all the way down to his feet without hurting him, till finally he bit him under the heel. This made *Oo-wel'-lin* kick. *Oo'-choom* waited, and when the giant had fallen asleep bit him under the heel of the other foot, and he kicked again. Then *Oo'-choom* told the people.

When the people heard this they took sharp sticks and long sharp splinters of stone and set them up firmly in the trail, and hid nearby and watched. After a while *Oo-wel'-lin* came back and stepped on the sharp points till the bottoms of his feet were stuck full of them. This hurt him dreadfully, and he fell down and died.

When he was dead the people asked, "Now he is dead, what are we to do with him?"

And they all answered that they did not know.

But a wise man said, "We will pack wood and make a big fire and burn him."

Then everyone said, "All right, let's burn him," and they brought a great quantity of dry wood and made a big fire and burned *Oo-wel'-lin* the Giant. When he began to burn, the wise man told everybody to watch closely all the time to see if any part should fly off to live again, and particularly to watch the whites of his eyes. So all the people watched closely all the time he was burning. His flesh did not fly off; his feet did not fly off; his hands did not fly off; but by and by the whites of his eyes flew off quickly – so quickly indeed that no one but *Chik'-chik* saw them go. *Chik'-chik* was a small bird whose eyes looked sore, but his sight was keen and quick. He was watching from a branch about twenty feet above the Giant's head and saw the whites of the eyes fly out. He saw them fly out and saw where they went and quickly darted after them and brought them back and put them in the fire again, and put on more wood and burnt them until they were completely consumed.

The people now made a hole and put *Oo-wel'-lin's* ashes in it and piled rocks on the place and watched for two or three days. But *Oo-wel'-lin* was dead and never came out.

Then the wise man asked each person what he would like to be, and called their names. Each answered what animal he would be, and forthwith turned into that animal and has remained the same to this day.

This was the beginning of the animals as they

are now – the deer, the ground squirrel, the bear, and other furry animals; the bluejay, the quail, and other birds of all kinds, and snakes and frogs and the yellowjacket wasp and so on.

Before that they were *Hoi-ah'-ko* – the FIRST PEOPLE.

Tim=me=la⁴le the Thunder

WHEN *Oo-wel'-lin* the Giant was traveling south over the country eating people, there were two little boys, brothers, who were out hunting when he was at their village, and so escaped. When they came home they found that their father and mother and all the other people had been killed and eaten.

The younger one asked the other, "What shall we do? Shall we live here, only two of us? Maybe you are clever enough to turn into some other kind of thing and never die."

The elder brother did not know; he was stupid; the younger was the bright one.

For about a month they hunted birds and ate them; they had no acorn mush or other food, nothing but birds. One day they made a little hut of brush (called *o-hoo'-pe*) by a spring where the birds came to drink. Here they killed a great many birds of different kinds.

The younger brother said, "Let us save all the feathers of the birds we kill—wing feathers and tail feathers and all."

Soon they had enough for both, and the younger said, "We have enough. Let's be big birds and never die—never grow old."

"How are we to do it?" asked the elder brother.

The younger answered, "You know how the big birds spread their wings and go, without bothering to eat or drink."

In a few days they took the big wing-feathers they had saved and stuck them in a row along their arms, and soon had wings; and then they stuck other feathers all over their bodies and soon were covered with feathers, like big birds.

Then the younger brother said: "You fly; let me see you fly a little way." The elder brother tried but could not make his wings go.

"Try again and I'll help," said the younger, and he pushed his brother along; but though he tried again he could not fly, and dropped down.

Then they took more feathers and set them closer so they would not leak air. When they had done this the younger asked: "Do you think you can go this time?"

But the elder one replied, "Let's see you try."

"All right," the younger answered, and flew a little way.

"Now you try," he called, and lifted his brother up and pushed him to help him start, but when he had flown a little way he cried out that he could not go any farther.

"Go on, I'm coming," called the younger, and he soon caught up and came under his brother and sailed round and round and went up into the air and came down.

174

The Orphan Boys killing Ducks and Geese by the River. "For a month they hunted birds and ate them."

Then the younger said, "Now we can fly, what kind of animal shall we be?"

The elder answered that he did not know.

The younger said, "How about *We-ho'-whe-mah*, who lives on the water in the back country?"

"All right," replied the other. So they flew again, and the younger helped start the elder and flew under him so as to catch him if he fell, and they flew up and down and around.

The younger again asked his brother if he would like to be *We-ho'-whe-mah*.

The brother replied, "No, I don't want to live on the water."

"Then how would you like to be *Tim-me-lā'-le* the Thunder," asked the younger. "We could come back sometimes and make a big noise and frighten the people. In summer we could go up through the north hole in the sky and stay up above the sky, and in winter come back here and make a big noise and rain to make the country green. Then maybe the people would come back and live again. We once had a father and mother and sister and uncle and grandfather and others. Maybe they would come back. We want to help them; we could make good rain to make things grow—acorns, pine nuts, grass, and all. Then maybe the people would come back and eat. We should never use food, never drink water, never grow old, and never be killed."

"All right," answered the elder, "We shall live always. But how are we going to make rain?"

"I'll show you," answered the younger. And they started again and went up very slowly, way up to the sky, and went north and found the north hole and went through it. When near the sky, but before they had gone through, the younger began to make a loud rumbling noise; it was *Tim-me-lā'-le* the Thunder.[18] The elder tried but failed. The younger told him to try again. He did so and in a short time made thunder all right. Then they went through the hole and up above the sky into the *Yel'-lo-kin* country.

When winter time came the younger said, "Come, let us go back." So they came down through the hole in the sky and traveled south and saw that people were there already. Then they shouted and made thunder and rain. After that they returned home through the north hole in the sky. And every winter even to this day they come back and thunder and make rain to make things grow for the people.

---

[18] *Tim-me-lā'-le* is rolling thunder; the sharp crash is *Kah'-loo.*

Wek'-wek's Search for his Father

AH-HA'-LE the Coyote-man told the people that there were four holes in the sky – one in the north, one in the south, one in the east, and one in the west. In those days *Tim-me-lā'-le* the Thunder came out of the north hole in winter and went back about May, just as he does now.

At this time *Wek'-wek* the Falcon was not yet born. His father, *Yi'-yil*, had gone far away to the south, where he had been killed before *Wek'-wek's* birth.

When *Wek'-wek* was fourteen years old he already had two or three wives, one of whom was *Yow'-hah* the Mallard Duck. He asked her if she was old enough to have seen his father. She replied, "No."

He then traveled all about and asked all the people who his father was and where he had gone, but no one could tell him. Then he went out to search; he traveled north, south, east, and west, but could find no trace of his father and no one could tell him where he had gone.

Then *Wek'-wek* transformed himself into a witch doctor and said, "Now I know where my father went, I smell him."

At sundown he came home to *Yow'-hah* his wife,

179

and when she had fallen asleep he took a forked limb of a tree and put it in the bed beside her. Then he went down into a hole in the ground and came up near the village [thus leaving no tracks]. Then he went south.

In the morning *Yow'-hah* awoke and found the forked limb and pushed it away saying, " What's the matter with my husband?" She asked his other wives if they had seen which way he went – "Which way did our husband go?" she asked.

They replied, " Go away, you live with him, we don't."

Then *Yow'-hah* went away and cried. She cried for a day or so, but no one could tell her which way *Wek'-wek* had gone.

She then took a crooked acorn stick and stuck it in the ground and the stick sprang south. Then she knew the way he had gone, and quickly prepared some baskets of food and set out to follow him.

After a while she overtook him, bringing him the food. By this time *Wek'-wek* was very tired and had fallen down on the side of the trail. He had a partner, *Hoo-loo'-e* the Dove, who accompanied him. He said to *Hoo-loo'-e*, " The old woman is coming behind; I am going to shoot her." But when she came he could not pull the arrow. She went to him and said, " You are hungry; I've brought you food."

He was angry and would not answer. He said

180

to *Hoo-loo'-e* his partner, "You are hungry, you had better eat."

Hoo-loo'-e replied, "Yes, I think I am hungry."

"Well, eat," said *Wek'-wek*, and *Hoo-loo'-e* ate.

Wek'-wek was angry and would not eat. He told his wife to go home and not follow him. He said: "I go to a bad place; I follow my father; nobody can get through the hole in the sky; you go home."

She answered, "No, I'll not go home, I'll follow you."

Then *Wek'-wek* continued on the trail of his father.

Wek'-wek had an aunt, *Ol'-lus muk-ki'-e* the Toad-woman. Her husband was *O-wah'-to*, the big-headed Fire Lizard. He had a fire which he could send to burn people.

Wek'-wek told *Hoo-loo'-e* his partner to go around another way with *Yow'-hah* his wife while he stopped to talk to his aunt's husband, *O-wah'-to*. Again he told his wife to go home, but she would not. Then *Wek'-wek* went to the place where *O-wah'-to* lived. He saw his aunt *Ol'-lus muk-ki'-e* outside, cracking acorns, and went to her to get something to eat.

O-wah'-to, who was inside the house, called out "Who's there?" and his wife answered, "Nobody." Then he heard *Wek'-wek* take another step, and called out again, "Who's there?" and again his wife answered, "Nobody, only *Oo'-choom* the Fly." She whispered to *Wek'-wek* to step very softly and to eat very quickly – to hurry and eat and go.

But *O-wah'-to* heard him and exclaimed, "Somebody is out there sure," and he came out and saw *Wek'-wek*, and sent his fire to burn him.

Wek'-wek ran and ran as fast as he could and caught up with *Hoo-loo'-e* and *Yow'-hah*, but the fire chased them and burnt so quickly and came so fast that they had not time to reach the hole in the sky. So they turned and ran down to the low country and climbed up on a high rock; but the fire kept on and burned the rock. Then they rushed to the ocean, but the fire dashed after them and made the water boil. Then they hastened north to another big rock, as high as a hill, and climbed on top; but the fire pursued and burnt that rock also. Then they climbed up into the sky, but the fire pressed on and came so close that it singed the tail of *Wek'wek's* quiver. Then they ran down into the low country again and found a crack in the ground and all three crawled into it. But the fire came and burnt down into the crack and drove them out.

By this time *Wek'-wek's* wife, *Yow'-hah*, had become very tired from so much running, and gave out. She said to her husband, "You are of no account. Why don't you put out that fire? I would like to see you make a pond half a mile wide."

"I'll try," he answered and shot an arrow of the *kow'-woo* wood (the buttonball bush) into the ground and water came up through the hole and continued to rise until they all stood in water, but still the fire beset them and made the water boil. *Yow'-hah* said she thought she would die. Then *Wek'-wek* shot an arrow into the ground in another place and a spring of water came and green stuff grew around the edges; but the fire continued and made the water boil as before.

Again *Yow'-hah* said, "You are of no account; you would die if I had not followed you."

Wek'-wek answered, "All right, you try."

Yow'-hah took a tule and threw it, and a big spring burst out, bordered all around with a broad belt of green tules; and they stepped into the spring and the fire could not reach them – it could not burn the green tules. So the fire went out and there was no more fire. *Yow'-hah* the old woman had stopped the fire. She was proud of this and said, "You see, if I had stayed at home you would be dead; if I go you will be all right." And the three continued on together.

By and by they came to the hole – the south hole in the sky. Then *Wek'-wek* said, "You two had better go home, you can't get through the hole."

His wife answered "No," and tried to go through but failed.

Wek'-wek shot an arrow through, but the hole closed so quickly that it caught the arrow and broke it. He again said to the others, "You can't get through." Then he tried and jumped so quickly that he went through. Then *Hoo-loo'-e* his partner tried, and likewise jumped very quickly and got through, and the sky did not catch him. Then *Yow'-hah* had to try again. *Wek'-wek* told her she must go through or go back. But she was too big and too slow. She said, "You will have to take me through." So he went back and got her and put her into his dog-skin quiver and jumped through with her. As they passed through, the hole closed and caught her feet and crushed them flat—that is why all ducks have flat feet.

Now all three were through.

In the south, beyond the hole in the sky, were other people. They had two chiefs, *Ho'-ho* the Turkey Buzzard, and *Koo'-choo* a huge shaggy beast of great strength and fierceness. *Tap-pitch'-koo-doot* the Kingbird lived there, and *Hok'-ke-hok'-ke* also.

Before *Wek'-wek* arrived, Captain *Ho'-ho* the Buzzard said to the people, "I dreamed that a north Indian is coming—the son of *Yï'-yil*, the man we burned. Everybody watch; maybe we shall have a good time again." So everybody watched.

After a while the watchers saw *Wek'-wek* coming. They saw him come through the hole. Then they ran back and told the people. This made the people happy, and they made ready to play the ball game.

When *Wek'-wek* reached the village he saw his father's widow there crying, with her hair cut short in mourning. He asked her, "Did my father die here?"

"Yes," she answered, and added, "Your father had plenty of money when he lost the game, but the chiefs *Koo'-choo* and *Ho'-ho* would not take the money; they were playing for his life; they wanted to burn him. Old *Koo'-choo* made a circle around the fire and made your father stand in the middle, and told him not to die too soon. After he had been burning a little while *Koo'-choo* asked how far the fire had burned, and *Yi'-yil* answered, 'to my knees, I'm going to die.'

"'No, don't die yet,' said *Koo'-choo*; and he asked again, 'How far has the fire burned now?'

"*Yi'-yil* answered, 'to my belly, and I'm going to die now.'

"'No, don't die yet,' said *Koo'-choo*, and he asked again, 'How far has the fire burned now?'

"'To my heart,' replied *Yi'-yil*, 'and I'm going to die now.'

"'No, no,' again said *Koo'-choo*, 'don't die yet; how far has the fire burned now?'

"'To my shoulders and I'm going to die,' said *Yi'yil*.

"'No, don't die yet; how far has the fire burned now?'

"'To my mouth, and I'm going to die,' answered *Yi'-yil*.

"'No, not yet, there's plenty of time yet,' said *Koo'-choo*; 'how far has it burned now?'

"'To my eyes, it's burning my eyes now and I'm going to die,' replied *Yi'-yil*.

"'No, no,' said *Koo'-choo*, 'don't die yet;' and when he saw that the fire had reached the top of *Yi'-yil's* head he asked again and for the last time, 'How far has it burned now?'

"There was no reply, and he knew, and all the people knew, that *Yi'-yil* was burned to death and was dead."

This is what *Yi'-yil's* widow, who had seen the burning, told *Wek'-wek*.

Wek'-wek was very angry; he knew that the people wanted to burn him as they had burned *Yi'-yil* his father; and he made up his mind what he would do. He left his wife *Yow'-hah* with *Koo'-choo* and the others and told her to entertain them. He then asked his father's widow which way they had taken his father to play the ball game. She told him, and he followed his father's trail. He found gopher holes in the trail, and holes the people had made for the ball to fall into so he would lose the game, and he filled them up. He came back over *Koo'-choo's* trail by daylight and found it all right—all the holes filled up and no holes left.

When he returned he found that the two firemen, *Lol'-luk* the Woodrat and *No-put'-kul-lol* the Screech Owl, had the fire all ready to burn him, but he said nothing.

Early next morning they all set out down the trail to play the ball game. *Wek'-wek* played so fast that old *Koo'-choo* became very tired and nearly gave out. He shot out a terrible skunk-like smell to make *Wek'-wek* sick, but *Wek'-wek* kept ahead and was not harmed.

Wek'-wek won the game and came back first; all the others were tired and *Koo'-choo* came in half dead.

When they had returned, *Yow'-hah, Wek'-wek's* wife, told *Wek'-wek* to burn *Koo'-choo* first.

Koo'-choo said to *Wek'-wek*: "You have won the game; everybody will bring you money; here is the money; you take it."

Wek'-wek answered, "No, I'll not take it. You would not take my father's money; you took his life."

Then they brought two more sacks full of money, but *Wek'-wek* pushed it away. He seized the two wicked chiefs, *Koo'-choo* and *Ho'ho*; he seized them by their arms and threw them into the fire that had been prepared for him, and took the others in the same way and threw them all in the fire. Some ran away and tried to hide, but *Wek'-wek* went after them and brought them back and threw them in the fire – men, women, and children – and burned them all. He then called the firemen to come – *Lol'-luk* the Woodrat and *No-put'-kul-lol* the Screech Owl – but they cried and refused to come. Then he took his bow and arrow and shot them and pitched them into the fire and they were burned like the rest.

The only people not burned were two witch doctors—*Pel-pel'-nah* the Nuthatch and *Choo-ta-tok'-kwe-lah* the Red-headed Sapsucker. They lived in the big ceremonial house and never came out; they never ate and never drank. *Wek'-wek* asked them, "Shall I come in?"

They answered "Yes."

Wek'-wek went inside and said: "You two are witch doctors; you never eat and never drink and never see people. Do you think you can make my father live again? I'll pay you. I want to see my father. I want to see what he is like."

They answered that they would try. One said to the other: "We will try; yes, we must try; but how shall we do it?" Then they took a jointed rod of *la'-hah* (the wild cane) and put *Yi'-yil's* burnt bones in the hollow inside, and put three or four feathers on the outside, like an arrow. Then *Choo-ta-tok'-kwe-lah* asked *Wek'-wek* for his bow, and took it and shot the cane arrow high up into the air; and when it was way up, *Yi'-yil* came slowly out of the hole in the end and sailed around and around, coming lower and lower, till he came down where the others were.

Then *Wek'-wek* asked him, "Are you my father? You don't look as I supposed."

Yi'-yil answered, "Yes, I'm *Yi'-yil* your father."

Wek'-wek said, " I've burned all the people here. Will you go home with me? Are you sure you are my father?"

"Yes," answered *Yi'-yil*, I'm your father and I'll go home with you."

"All right," said *Wek'-wek*, " Let's go."

After a while, when they had gone a little way, *Wek'-wek* turned and said, " I think you had better not go with me. You look queer—only half like us. You go to the other side of the mountain down on the coast" (meaning *Oo'-yum-bel'-le*, Mount Diablo). Then *Yi'-yil* went back into the cane arrow, and *Wek'-wek*, his wife *Yow'-hah*, and his partner *Hoo-loo'-e* returned through the hole in the sky that they had gone through on their way south.

When they were on the other side, *Wek'-wek* said to his wife: "Old woman, you may have to run again. I'm going to kill *O-wah'-to*, my uncle-in-law, who chased us with fire and tried to destroy us when we were here before." So he sent *Yow'-hah* and *Hoo-loo'-e* ahead and told them to wait for him while he proceeded to *O-wah'-to's* place. He went there and shot *O-wah'-to* with an arrow and killed him dead the first shot.

Then they continued on, and when they had gone a few miles, they came to another fireman, whose name was *Hos-sok'-kil-wah*. *Wek'-wek* sent his wife and partner ahead as before while he went alone to fight *Hos-sok'-kil-wah*. He took an arrow with a point of white flint stone, and shot and killed *Hos-sok'-kil-wah*, who at once turned into the white flint fire rock. And so they continued, *Wek'-wek* killing all the bad people on the way.

189

11

Wek=wek's Search for his Sister

AFTER *Wek'-wek, Hoo-loo'-e* and *Yow'-hah* had returned home, *Wek'-wek* said, "I have heard that I once had a sister; where is my sister?"

No one answered.

Then *Wek'-wek* slept and dreamed. Then he went off alone to the north and told no one.

Wek'-wek had a nephew, *Ah'-ut* the Crow. *Ah'-ut* asked the people, "Where is my uncle?" No one answered. Then *Ah'-ut* said he would find him, and he also set out for the north. Finding that he could not catch up with *Wek'-wek* he shot an arrow and the arrow went over *Wek'-wek's* head and fell just beyond.

Wek'-wek knew who had shot it, and said, "Who told my nephew?"

When *Ah'-ut* came up, *Wek'-wek* asked, "Why do you follow me? I'm searching for my sister; you go home."

"No," answered *Ah'-ut*, "I'll go with you."

Then *Wek'-wek's* brothers, two little hawks, who also had been following, overtook *Wek'-wek* and *Ah'-ut* and all went on together.

After a while they found the rancheria. It was in a big cave about two miles below *Koo-loo'-te* [now the town of Sonora in Tuolumne County]. *Wek'-wek* sent one of his little brothers into the cave. He went in and on one side of the entrance saw *O-hum'-mah-te* the Grizzly Bear, and on the other side *He-le'-jah* the Mountain Lion, but saw nothing of the sister.

Then *Wek'-wek* sent in the other brother. When he returned he said some one was inside cooking acorns; he had seen a woman cook the acorn soup by putting into the basket hot quail eggs instead of hot stones. He said also that farther back in the cave was something that looked like a sharp rock.

Then *Ah'-ut* the Crow said he would go in. When he found the woman cooking with the quail eggs he picked them up and took off the shells and ate all the eggs. Then he asked the woman, "Is my uncle's sister here?"

"Yes," she answered, "but you can't go in."

But he did go in, and when he came to *He-le'-jah* the Mountain Lion, he said, "You are good to eat," and shot him with an arrow and killed him. Then he turned to *O-hum'mah-te* the Grizzly Bear and said the same to him, and killed him also and pulled him out. Then he went in farther and saw the Sharp Rock and shot it also and killed it, and picked up his arrow and put it back in his quiver. Then he went still farther in and found *Wek'-wek's* sister. She was old and naked and shriveled – nothing but bare bones – for no one had given her anything to eat.

Ah'-ut returned and told *Wek'-wek* he could now go in, and *Wek'-wek* went in. When he saw his sister without clothes and all bones he felt badly and cried. Then he took her out and helped her walk, and cooked some acorns and fed her. Then he sent her home with his brothers.

Wek=wek's Visit to the Underworld People

AFTER *Wek'-wek* had sent his sister home he stayed near the caves below *Koo-loo'-te* and dug holes in the sand and found roots and seeds that were good to eat. In digging he came to a very deep hole which led down under the world; he went down this hole and when he reached the underworld found other people there, and got a wife with a little boy. Besides his wife there were *To-to'-kon* the Sandhill Crane, *Wah'-ah* the Heron, *Cha-poo'-kah-lah* the Blackbird, and others.

To-to'-kon the Sandhill Crane was chief. When he saw *Wek'-wek* he said, "What shall we do with this man; he is lost; we had better kill him."

Wek'-wek saw a man make ready with his bow and arrow, and invited him to come and eat. The man came and ate, and when his belly was full went back.

Captain *To-to'-kon* said, "I didn't send you to eat, but to kill him." Then he sent another, and *Wek'-wek* asked him also to come and eat, and he did as the other had done. Then Captain *To-to'-kon* sent two men together to kill him, but *Wek'-wek* called them both to come and eat, and they did so. Then *To-to'-kon* was angry; he sent no more

195

men but went himself and took his bow and arrow.

Wek'-wek said to him, "Come in," whereupon *To-to'-kon* shot his arrow but missed.

Then *Wek'-wek* came out and faced the people. They fired all their arrows but could not kill him. *Wek'-wek* said, "You can't kill me with arrows. Have you a pot big enough to hold me?"

"Yes," they answered.

"Then set it up and put me in it," he said.

And they did as they were told and put *Wek'-wek* in the hot pot and put the cover on. When he was burned they took out the burnt bones and buried them in the ground.

Ah'-ut the Crow missed his uncle and went to his uncle's partner, *Hoo-loo'-e*, who was in the hole crying, and asked where *Wek'-wek* was. *Hoo-loo'-e* pointed down the hole. *Ah'-ut* went down and found the rancheria of the underworld people and killed them all. He then asked *Wek'-wek's* wife where *Wek'-wek* was. She answered that the people had burned and buried him.

Wek'-wek stayed in the ground five days and then came to life; he came out and asked his wife where the people were. She told him that *Ah'-ut* had come and killed them all. "That is too bad," he exclaimed, "I wanted to show them what kind of man I am." Then he said she should stay there and he would take the boy and go home.

She answered, "All right."

Then he shot his arrow up through the hole and

caught hold of it, and held the boy also, and the arrow carried them both up to the upper world.

TAH'-LOW THE THUNDER AND TAH'-KIP' THE LIGHTNING

FRAGMENT OF A STORM MYTH OF THE HOO'-KOO-E'-KO OF NICASIO AND TOMALES BAY

PERSONAGES

Tah'-low the Thunder
Tah'-kip' the Lightning
Koo-lā'-is kā'-sum the Mother Deer
O'-ye the Coyote-man
Koo'-le the Bear
Oo'-pah the Rain

Tah=low the Thunder and Tah=kip′ the Lightning

KOO-LA′-IS KA′-SUM the mother Deer died, leaving two boy fawns. Their uncle, *O′-ye* the Coyote-man, sent them away to the east, where they still live.

Once when the country was very dry an old woman who wanted water, but could not find any, went and looked at the boy fawns, and they tore her eyes out. That made *Tah′-kip′* the Lightning. Then they took the dry skin of *Koo′-le* the Bear, and shook it. That made *Tah′-low* the Thunder. Then *Oo′-pah* the Rain came.

HE'-KOO-LAS THE SUN-WOMAN
A TALE OF THE HOO'-KOO-E'-KO OF TOMALES BAY

PERSONAGES
He'-koo-lās the Sun-woman
O'ye the Coyote-man

He'-koo-las the Sun-woman

THE world was dark. The only light any-
where was *He'-koo-lās* the Sun-woman. She
lived far away in the east.

The people wanted light, and *O'-ye* the Coyote-
man sent two men to bring *He'-koo-lās*. They
traveled a long time, for they had far to go. When
they came to the place where she lived she refused
to go back with them. So they came back alone
and told *O'-ye*.

Then he sent more men; this time he sent enough
men to bring her whether she wanted to come or
not. They made the long journey to her home and
tied her with ropes and brought her back to make
light for the people.

Her entire body was covered with *ah'-wook* – the
beautiful iridescent shells of the abalone; these
made her shine so brightly that she gave off light
and it was hard to look at her.

HOW O'-YE THE COYOTE-MAN DISCOVERED HIS WIFE
A TALE OF THE HOO'-KOO-E'-KO OF NICASIO AND SAN RAFAEL

PERSONAGES

O'-ye the Coyote-man
Wek'-wek the Falcon, *O'-ye's* grandson
Ko-to'-lah the Frog-woman

How O'-ye the Coyote-man discovered his Wife

THE world was made by *O'-ye* the Coyote-man. The earth was covered with water. The only thing that showed above the water was the very top of *Oon'-nah-pi's* [Sonoma Peak, about forty miles north of San Francisco].

In the beginning *O'-ye* came on a raft from the west, from across the ocean. His raft was a mat of tules and split sticks; it was long and narrow. *O'-ye* landed on the top of *Oon'-nah-pi's* and threw his raft-mat out over the water – the long way north and south, the narrow way east and west; the middle rested on the rock on top of the peak. This was the beginning of the world and the world is still long and narrow like the mat – the long way north and south, the narrow way east and west.

When *O'-ye* was sitting alone on top of *Oon'-nah-pi's*, and all the rest of the world was covered with water, he saw a feather floating toward him, blown by the wind from the west – the direction from which he himself had come. He asked the feather, "Who are you?"

The feather made no reply.

He then told the feather about his family and all his relatives. When he came to mention *Wek'-*

wek, his grandson, the feather leaped up out of the water and said, " I am *Wek'-wek*, your grandson."

O'-ye the Coyote-man was glad, and they talked together.

Every day *O'-ye* noticed *Ko-to'-lah* the Frog-woman sitting near him. Every time he saw her he reached out his hand and tried to catch her, but she always jumped into the water and escaped.

After four days the water began to go down, leaving more land on top of the mountain, so that *Ko-to'-lah* had to make several leaps to reach the water. This gave *O'-ye* the advantage and he ran after her and caught her. When he had caught her he was surprised to find that she was his own wife from over the ocean. Then he was glad.

When the water went down and the land was dry *O'-ye* planted the buckeye and elderberry and oak trees, and all the other kinds of trees, and also bushes and grasses, all at the same time. But there were no people and he and *Wek'-wek* wanted people. Then *O'-ye* took a quantity of feathers of different kinds, and packed them up to the top of *Oon'-nah-pi's* and threw them up into the air and the wind carried them off and scattered them over all the country and they turned into people, and the next day there were people all over the land.

NOTE. The above story was told me at Tomales Bay by an aged *Hookooeko* woman, now dead, who in her early life lived at Nicasio. Another old woman, who originally came from San Rafael, gave me a slightly different version. She said that *O'-ye* the Coyote-man made the feathers up into four bundles, which he set in the ground in four different places – one in the west, at San Rafael; one in the east, at Sonoma; one in the north, near Santa Rosa, and one in the south, on the south side of San Francisco Bay. Next morning all had turned into people, each bundle becoming a distinct tribe, speaking a language wholly different from the languages of the others.

12

Part 2: Present Day Myths

In addition to the Ancient Myths or FIRST PEOPLE stories, which relate to the early history of the world, the Mewan tribes have numerous beliefs concerning the present and the very recent past. Some of these – mainly fragments or outlines, but covering a wide range of subjects – have been collected from nearly all the extant tribes and are here brought together. They are arranged under the following headings: Beliefs concerning Animals; Beliefs concerning Ghosts and the Sign of Death; Beliefs concerning Natural Phenomena; Beliefs concerning Witches, Pigmies, Giants, and other Fabulous Beings.

Beliefs concerning Animals

BEARS RESEMBLE PEOPLE AND LIKE TO DANCE

The Northern Mewuk say:

Bears are like people. They stand up, they have hands, and when the hide is off, their bodies look like the bodies of people. Bears know a great deal. They understand the Mewuk language, and their hearing is so sharp that they hear a person a long way off and know what he says.

Bears, like people, like to dance. Once an old Indian saw some bears dance in the forest. He saw *Oo-soo'-ma-te* the old she Grizzly Bear and a lot of little bears. The old she Bear leaned up against a young pine tree with her left hip and bent it down, and sang *moo'-oo, moo'-oo.* The little bears caught hold of the bent-over tree, hanging on with their hands over their heads, while they danced with their hind feet on the ground.

HOW HE-LE'-JAH THE COUGAR HUNTS DEER

The Northern Mewuk say:

He-le'-jah the Cougar is a hunter. He hunts *O-woo'-yah* the Deer. He crawls toward it like a cat, without making any noise; and when near enough makes a big leap and catches it, or knocks it down with his long tail. When he has killed the

Deer he throws his long tail around it, and packs it off on his back.

How Too-le'-ze, the Timber-wolf hunts Deer

The Northern Mewuk say:

Too-le'-ze the Big Wolf is a hunter. Like *He-le'-jah* the Cougar or Mountain Lion he hunts Deer, but he hunts in a different way. He chases them like *Choo'-koo* the Dog but catches them by the throat with his claws, which he sinks deep into the sides of the throat. In the early morning he howls long howls. He used to be common here but now is rarely seen.

Too'-cha-mo, the Stump, and Choo'-koo Heng-il'-nah-as'-se, the Lost Dog

The Northern Mewuk say:

Too'-cha-mo the stump and *Choo'-koo* the dog are friends. When *Choo'-koo* is lost and does not know where his man has gone he goes to *Too'-cha-mo* and asks. *Too'-cha-mo* tells him which way to go to strike his man's trail; *Choo'-koo* goes and finds it, and no matter how far away his man is, he follows the trail right to him.

The First Teeth go to Soo-wah-tah, the Gopher

The Middle Mewuk of Tuolumne River say:

When a child sheds its first teeth they should be

saved and taken to *Soo-wah-tah* the Pocket Gopher, and carefully put into his hole. Then the second teeth will come quickly and grow to be strong and good.

O-LEL′-LE THE MYSTERIOUS BIRD OF THE COLD SPRINGS

The Southern Mewuk of Mariposa region say:

Many people wear a *Wep′-pah* (amulet) around their necks to bring good luck and keep harm away. Some wear lucky stones, some lucky shells, some a forked feather—particularly the forked feather of a Bluejay, which is very lucky.

But the luckiest feather in the world, and the luckiest thing in the world, is a feather from *O-lel′-le*. *O-lel′-le* is a bird about the size of a Flicker, but no one ever had a good look at him. He lives in cold springs, down deep under the water, and sometimes makes the water bubble, and sometimes makes it muddy. He comes to the spring just at dark and dives down without stopping on top. In the morning just at daylight he comes up and jumps out of the water and flies away quickly, so it is very hard to see him.

Sometimes, once in a great while, a person finds one of *O-lel′-le's* feathers at the spring. This makes the strongest *Wep′-pah* in the world, and the person who finds it wears it on a string around his neck as long as he lives and always has good luck.

Soo-koo'-me the Great Horned Owl

The Middle Mewuk of Tuolumne River foothills say:

When *Soo-koo'-me* the Great Horned Owl hoots, it means that someone is dying. He is himself the Ghosts of dead people.[20]

[I was once asked by a Northern Mewuk if I had ever seen the broad belt of bony plates which surrounds the eyeball of the Great Horned Owl. On replying that I had, I was assured that these closely imbricating plates are the "finger nails all jammed tight together of the ghosts caught by the owl."]

The Meadowlark, a Gossip and Trouble-maker

The Olayome of Putah Creek say:

Hoo-yu'-mah the Meadowlark understands and speaks our language. He often makes disagreeable remarks; we often hear him say, "I see you are angry," and other mean things.

NOTE. In the Ancient Myths it has already been shown that the Northern Me'-wuk and Wi'-pā tribes of Mewan stock, and the Pā'-we-nan tribe of Midoo stock, hold the Meadowlark responsible for the failure of dead people to rise on the third or fourth day and come to life again (see pages

---

[20] For additional matter on this subject see Beliefs concerning Ghosts, pages 217-221. Similar beliefs are held by other California tribes.

55-56 and 132). This belief is widespread among the Mewan tribes and is held also by at least one Pomo tribe – the 'Ham'-fo or Koi'-im-fo of Clear Lake.

All the Mewan tribes, and many belonging to widely different stocks – including even the Washoo of Lake Tahoe and adjacent valleys east of the Sierra – class the Meadowlark among the bad birds. They say he talks too much and is a gossip and they do not like him. The Washoo call him *Se-soo'-te'-al-le* and, like several other tribes, insist that he talks to them in their own language and always makes uncomplimentary remarks. He tells them that he sees right through them; that they are stingy and provide only food enough for themselves; that they are dark on the outside only and under the skin are as white and mean as a white man, and so on.

The Mariposa Mewuk say:

If a person breaks a Meadowlark's egg it will rain.

Ki'-ki'-ah the Mountain Bluejay

The Middle Mewuk of Stanislaus River region say:

Ki'-ki'-ah, the Crested Bluejay of the mountains, plants acorns so that oak trees come up almost everywhere.

[Several other tribes mention the same habit which, by the way, is hardly a myth.]

213

WHERE THE DUCKS AND GEESE GO TO BREED

The Hookooeko of Tomales Bay say:

The home of Ducks and Geese is far up the coast in the cold country called *Kon'-win*, the North, which is on the other side of the sky. The way to this country lies between two high hills which continually go apart and come together, forming a sliding gateway which is ever opening and closing – the hills are never still.[21]

The name of these sliding hills is *Wal-le-kah'-pah.*

In spring when the Ducks and Geese go north they pass between the *Wal'-le-kah'-pah* hills and make their nests and rear their young in the cold *Kon'-win* country beyond; in fall they come back through the same opening and bring their young with them.

PO'-KO-MOO THE POISON SPIDER

The Northern Mewuk say:

Po'-ko-moo the small black spider with a red spot under his belly is poison.[22] Sometimes he scratches people with his long fingers, and the scratch makes a bad sore.

---

[21] The gateway in this little story is of course the North Hole in the sky, which is always described as opening and closing with great rapidity, so that only the swiftest personages can shoot through.

The *Wal'-le-kah'-pah* hills at the north opening are evidently the same as the Thunder Mountain of other tribes, which is always close by the north hole in the sky, in the region of extreme cold.

[22] This is true. The name of the poison spider is *Lathrodectus mactens.*

[All the tribes know that this spider is poisonous and some of them make use of the poison.]

WHERE KOO'-TAH THE MONEY-CLAM CAME FROM

The Olamentko of Bodega Bay say:

Coyote-man brought *Koo'-tah* the big clam, from which *pis'-pe* the shell money is made, and planted it here at Bodega Bay.[23]   This is the place and the only place where the big clam was in the beginning. Wherever else you find it now, the seed came from here.   The Tomales Bay people got their seed here.

---

[23] The large thick shell Bodega Bay clam from which shell money is made is *Saxidomus giganteus.*

Beliefs concerning Ghosts and the Sign of Death

GHOSTS FOLLOW THE PATHWAY OF THE WIND

The Hookooeko of Nicasio and Tomales Bay say:

When a person dies his *Wal'-le*[24] or Ghost goes to *Hel'-wah* the West, crossing the great ocean to *Oo-tā-yo'-me*, the Village of the Dead. In making this long journey it follows *hinnan mooka*, the path of the Wind. Sometimes Ghosts come back and dance in the roundhouse; sometimes people hear them dancing inside but never see them.

THREE BIRDS SCREAM TO FRIGHTEN THE GHOSTS

The Southern Mewuk of the Chowchilla region say:

After a person dies his *Hoo'-ne* or Ghost sets out toward the ocean. On the way it has to cross a broad river on a log. While it is crossing on this log, three birds scream to frighten it—*Hek-ek'-ke* the Quail, *Ha-chah'-we* the Barn Owl, and *Hah'-jen-nah* a small Heron.

---

[24] In this connection it is interesting to observe that in the language of the related *Olayome* of Putah Creek, Bats are called *Walle*; while the same word in the language of the Mewan Valley tribes means Ocean. The word for ocean among the Northern Mewuk is *Wallasu*; among the Middle or Tuolumne Mewuk, *Wallesmah*.

If the Ghost is frightened and falls into the river it turns into a fish; but if it keeps on and crosses the log it continues westerly over the ocean and goes to the place where all the Ghosts live together, and never comes back.

GHOSTS MAY COME BACK IN SOO-KOO'-ME THE OWL

The Middle Mewuk of Tuolumne River say:

When a person dies, *Oo'leus* the heart-spirit remains in the dead body for four days. During these four days everyone is quiet and the children are not allowed to run about or make a noise. On the morning of the fourth day the people sprinkle ashes on the ground over the buried basket of burnt bones – or over the grave if the corpse were buried instead of burned. On that day the heart spirit leaves the body in the invisible form of *Hinnan Soos* the Wind Spirit, or *Soo-les'-ko* the Ghost, and proceeds westward. That night it may come back in *Soo-koo'-me* the Owl, or in some other animal; so look out.

Some Ghosts are good, others bad. At last they all go to the ocean and cross over on a long pole to the Roundhouse of the dead, where they remain.

A HOLE IN THE NOSE SAVES TURNING INTO A FISH

The Southern Mewuk of the Mariposa region say:

If a person dies without a hole in his nose he will turn into a fish, but if the nose is perforated

218

for the *kun-no-wah* [25] he will not turn into a fish.

WHAT GOOD AND BAD GHOSTS TURN INTO

The Northern Mewuk say:

The heart-spirits or Ghosts (*Soo-lek'-ko*) of good Indians turn into *Too-koo'-le* the Great Horned Owl; those of bad Indians into *Et-tā'-le* the Barn Owl, *Yu'-kal-loo* the Meadowlark, *O-lā'-choo* the Coyote, or *Choo'-moo-yah* the Gray Fox.[26] Whatever they turn into they continue to be forever – there is no change after that.

The night after the Ghost leaves the body it may come back and do harm to someone – so it is well to look out. [My informant told me that the night after his wife's Ghost left her body it came back while he was asleep and beat him severely.]

NOTE. The Tribes of Midoo stock also believe in transmigration. The *No-to'-koi-yo* or North-eastern Midoo say that their ghosts go into the Great Horned Owl, while the *Pā'-we-nan* or South-western Midoo say that when a person dies his spirit (*oos*) may go into any one of a number of things: it may turn into an Owl or Coyote, a Snake or a Lizard; it may become a Whirlwind, or it may

---

[25] The *kun-no-wah* is a short white rod of shell or stone worn in the nose by both men and women of this tribe.

[26] The Coyote and Fox are bad – they kill too much and make too much trouble; good Indians do not like them. *Yu'-kal-loo* the Meadowlark is a bad bird; he is mean and is always saying disagreeable things.

go into the ground and become earth. Sometimes, but rarely, it goes off to a good place.

GHOSTS HIDE IN STUMPS AND WHIRLWINDS

The Northern Mewuk say:

Sometimes when passing *Too'-cha-mo* the stump you hear a noise inside; it is *Soo-lek'-ko* the Ghost. You had better go right on, for if you stop he might do you harm.

Whenever you see *Poo'-ki-yu* the Whirlwind whirling the dust around and around and carrying it up into the air you may know that *Soo-lek'-ko* the Ghost is inside, dancing and swinging round and round. You had better not go near it but keep away.

GHOSTS HUNT FOR A BIG ANIMAL IN THE OCEAN

The Mokalumne say:

After a person dies and is buried the heart-spirit comes out and shakes itself to shake off the earth, and then sails away in the air and disappears – going northwest to the ocean. This may happen on the fourth night, or at any time between the first and fourth.

The Ghost goes to the ocean and enters the water and finds a large animal [probably a whale] whose breast it immediately lays hold of and sucks. If it does not take the breast of this animal it can not live in the ocean with the other Ghosts, but in from two to four days returns and reënters the body from which it came, and comes back to life again. It then tells the old people of the beautiful things it saw in the ocean – flowers and fishes and animals.

For a long time the people did not know where the *Ul'-le* or Ghosts went. After a while the Napa Indians told our people that they sometimes heard strange noises in the air overhead, usually in the evening or very early morning, sometimes at night, and more rarely in the daytime. The sounds were sometimes like singing, sometimes like crying, sometimes like calling or scolding – always high up. For a long time they did not know what these noises were, but finally some wise Indians found out that they were the Ghosts of people from the interior passing over on their way to the ocean.

One of our people was a 'Half Doctor'; he knew much medicine and was a good dancer. Once, when some one died, the 'Half Doctor' made up his mind that he would find out about the Ghost. So after dark he went to the place and hid close to the grave and watched. In the night he saw something like a person get up out of the ground and shake his head to shake the earth off, and then fly away quickly, disappearing at once. Nothing more was seen.

WAH-TIB'-SAH THE SIGN OF DEATH

The Northern Mewuk of the Mokelumne River foothills say:

When a person feels the inner side of the calf

of his leg twitch, as if some one were poking it with his finger, it is a sure sign that within three days somebody is going to die, and he must take care that he is not the one. The twitching is done by the person's totem or guardian spirit, who comes and pokes his leg to warn him of the danger.[27]

[My informant, the chief of a small rancheria, told me that he had been thus warned several times by *Mā'-wā* the Gray Squirrel, who was his totem, and that each time some one had died. He told me also that an old blind woman who lived in the rancheria, and whose totem was a Yellow-jacket wasp, had more than once saved his life by whispering to him just as he was going somewhere, that she had felt *Wah-tib'-sah* and he had better not go. Her totem friend, *Mel'-ling-i'-yah* the Yellow-jacket, had come and poked her leg to warn her that somebody must die. He had always heeded her warning and stayed at home and was still alive, while some one else, in a neighboring rancheria, had died.]

---

[27] For remarks on the prevalence and significance of totemism among the Mewan tribes, see my article entitled "Totemism in California," *American Anthropologist*, vol. x, 558-561, 1908.

Beliefs concerning Natural Phenomena

THUNDER

*The Northern Mewuk near South Fork Cosumnes
River say:*

Tim'-mel-le the Thunder is, or is like, *Ti'-e-te*
the Valley Bluejay. He lives down below [west]
in the San Joaquin Valley, where the clouds are.
Sometimes he becomes angry and makes a great
rumbling noise; this noise is *Tim'-mel-le* the Thunder.[28]

THE RAINBOW

The Northern Mewuk say:

Ku-yet'-tah the Rainbow comes to tell the people
a baby is born. When anyone sees *Ku-yet'-tah* he
knows that somewhere a new baby has come. Everybody knows that.

The Hookooeko of Nicasio and Tomales Bay say:

Kah-chah the Rainbow is the bow of *O'-ye* the
Coyote-man.

THE EARTHQUAKE

The Olāyome of Putah Creek say:

Under the earth is a great giant named *He-*

---

[28] For additional beliefs about Thunder, see First People stories, pages
173-178; 199.

223

wow'-wah-tin. When angry he shakes the earth, causing *Yo'-wan-hew'-wah* the Earthquake.

NOISE

The Tuolumne Mewuk say:

In the beginning all noise came from water – running water. [Their word for shouting is *Wah-kah-lah'-loo*, derived from *Wah-kah'-loo*, river.]

The Northern Mewuk also say:

All noise came in the beginning from running water; the echo originally came from rapids or boisterous water.

Other tribes say:

Singing came from running water – the first song was sung by the creek.

THE ECHO

The Hookooeko of Nicasio and Tomales Bay say:

Pe-tān'-yah the Lizard with blue sides [29] lives everywhere in the rocks and hills and woods. When he hears a loud noise he talks back. This is *Si-yu-kā-i* the Echo; it is *Pe-tān'-yah* talking back.

The Olāyome of Putah Creek say:

Loo-te'-nek'-kah the Echo is *Pe-tā'-le* the blue-sided Lizard talking back.

---

[29] The blue-sided lizard meant is *Sceloporus occidentalis,* a common species in the coast region of California.

The Olamentko of Bodega Bay say:
The Echo is *Sah-kah'-te* talking back.

HOW THE WORLD GREW

The Northern Mewuk say:

In the beginning the world was rock. Every year the rains came and fell on the rock and washed off a little; this made earth. By and by plants grew on the earth and their leaves fell and made more earth. Then pine trees grew and their needles and cones fell every year and with the other leaves and bark made more earth and covered more of the rock.

If you look closely at the ground in the woods you will see how the top is leaves and bark and pine needles and cones, and how a little below the top these are matted together, and a little deeper are rotting and breaking up into earth. This is the way the world grew — and it is growing still.

Beliefs concerning Witches, Pigmies, Giants, and other Fabulous Beings

How Witches Kill People

The Hookooeko of Nicasio and San Rafael say:

Our country is on the north side of San Francisco Bay and reaches from San Rafael to Tomales Bay. Before the white man came and destroyed us there used to be witches among the people. The people used to burn the dead. Sometimes after a burning the witches would save the ashes and burnt bones (called *me'-cham yem'-me-um*) and pound them up fine in a stone mortar and use them to kill with. The witches had two ways of killing people. One way was to put the powdered bones and ashes on the windward side of the house or rancheria of the person they wished to harm. Then the wind would blow the fine dust over the enemy. Next day he would have a headache and feel sick, and every day grow worse until by and by he died.

Another way was to take the hollow wing bone of a Turkey-buzzard and go to windward of the person to be injured. The witch then blew through the bone toward the person. The person soon had bad dreams and felt lonesome, and next day went crazy, and after a while died.

With the right kind of a buzzard bone (called *to'-kah*) a witch could blow harm to a person from a distance as great as two miles.

PIGMIES AND WATER PEOPLE

The Hookooeko of Nicasio and Tomales Bay say:

Se'-kah the Little Folk dwell in thick places in the dark redwood forest, where no people live. They are very small. Sometimes they make people crazy.

Le'-wah ke'-lak the Water People live in the ocean, in a roundhouse under the water; sometimes they come up and show themselves.

THE DEVIL OF SAN RAFAEL

The Hookooeko of San Rafael say:

Yu'-ten me'-chah the Evil One lives in the hills just north of San Rafael; he travels about at night and sometimes comes and touches people when they are asleep, to frighten them.

HO-HA'-PE THE RIVER MERMAID

The Southern Mewuk of Merced River foothills say:

Some of the rivers are inhabited by *Ho-hā'-pe*, the River Mermaids or Water Women. The *Ho-hā'-pe* have long hair and are beautiful to look at. They usually live in deep pools, and are known at several places in *Wah-kal'-mut-tah* (Merced

River). In that part of the river which runs through *Ah-wah'-ne* (Yosemite Valley) they have been seen a number of times.

One lives now lower down in the river, at the upper end of Pleasant Valley in the large round pool called *Ow'-wal*. In the early days two partners used to fish for salmon at *Ow'-wal*, one on each side of the pool; several times they saw *Ho-hā'-pe*.

Another lives in the deep water at *Wel'-le-to* (on the Barrett ranch, a little below Pleasant Valley). At this place a few years ago some Indians from Bear Valley and Coulterville came to catch salmon. They put their net in a deep place in the river, and when it was full of fish tried to pull it out, but could not, for it was stuck on the bottom. *Ho-hā'-pe* the Water Woman had fastened it to a rock, but the men did not know this. One of them went down to find where the net had caught, and to lift it up. While he was doing this *Ho-hā'-pe* put a turn of the net-rope around his big toe and he was drowned. Then several of the men had to go down to get him. After they brought up his body all of them saw *Ho-hā'-pe* in the pool below, and saw her long hair float out in the current.

NOTE — The story of *Ho-hā'-pe* the River Mermaid, varying more or less in details, reaches north at least to American River, where the Nissenan (who call her *Ho-sā'-pah*) have the following version:

Two maidens were walking along American River below the foothills when they heard a baby cry. They followed the sound and soon saw the baby lying on a sand bar in the edge of the river. One of them reached down to pick it up when it suddenly changed to *Ho-sā'-pah* the River Mermaid, who, seizing the young woman, dragged her into the river. She cried out and her companion took hold of her arm and pulled and pulled as hard as she could to save her, but *Ho-sā'-pah* was the stronger and dragged her under the water and she was never seen again.

The other maiden ran home to the village and told her people what had happened. She was so terribly frightened that her mind became affected and in a short time she died.

THE ROCK GIANTS

CHE-HA-LUM'-CHE THE ROCK GIANT OF CALAVERAS COUNTY

The Northern Mewuk say:

Che-ha-lum'-che the Rock Giant carries on his back a big burden basket (*che'-ka-la*) which, like himself, is of rock. He lives in caves, of which there are two near Mountain Ranch or El Dorado in Calaveras County, one at Murphys, and one on Stanislaus River.

Che-ha-lum'-che comes out only at night and wanders about seeking *Mewuk* [people] to eat. He prefers women; of these he catches and carries off all he can find. Sometimes he makes a crying noise, *hoo-oo'-oo* like a baby, to lure them. If they come he seizes them and tosses them into his big pack basket and carries them to his cave, where he eats them. In the basket is a long spike which pierces their bodies when they are thrown in, so they can not escape.

In his caves are the remains of his victims — horns of deer and bones of people and different kinds of animals.

Indians never throw their dead into caves. If they did, *Che-ha-lum'-che* would get them. Any

231

man who would put a dead person in a cave would be killed by the other Indians.[30]

Oo'-le the Rock Giant of the Chowchilla Foothills

The Southern Mewuk say:

Far away in the west, in the place where the sun goes down, lived *Oo'-le* the Rock Giant. At night he used to come up into the foothills to catch people and eat them.

Loo-poo-oi'-yes the Rock Giant of Tamalpais

The Hookooeko of Nicasio and San Rafael say:

A woman had a husband and two boy babies—

---

[30] Many human skulls and skeletons have been found in caves along the west slope of the middle Sierra. The presence of human remains in these caves has been interpreted to mean that the Indians now living in the region practise cave burial, or did practise it until recent times. This is an error. The Indians of this region, the Mewuk, burned their dead, and look with horror on the suggestion that they or their ancestors might ever have put their dead in caves. They ask: "Would you put your mother, or your wife, or your child, or any one you love, in a cave to be eaten by a horrible giant?" The idea is so abhorrent to them that the theory of cave burial must be abandoned as preposterous.

The mythology of the Mewuk does not admit of any migration but describes the creation of the people in the area they still inhabit. This, in connection with the fact that these Indians speak a language wholly different from any known in any other part of the world, proves that they have occupied the lands they now occupy for a very long period – a period which in my judgment should be measured by thousands of years.

This argues a great antiquity for the cave remains, for they must be those of a people who inhabited the region before the Mewuk came – and this takes us back a very long way into the past.

Che'-ha-lum'-che the Rock Giant catching People to eat

twins. The woman's brother killed her husband and the little boys did not know that they ever had a father. When they were big enough they went off every day to play by a big rock in the woods. They went always to the same place; they liked this place and always went there. This was the very place where their father, when he was alive, used to go every day to sing, but the little boys did not know this – for they did not even know that they had ever had a father.

One day the boys heard somebody say: "You come here every day just as your father used to." The voice came from the rock; it was the voice of *Loo'-poo-oi'-yes* [31] the Rock Giant. Then the boys knew they had had a father. They went to the rock and saw long hairs sticking up. These hairs grew out of the nostrils of *Loo'-poo-oi'-yes*; the boys took hold of them and pulled them out.

This made *Loo'-poo-oi'-yes* angry and he took a long hooked stick and tried to catch the boys to kill them. He was all rock except a place on his throat where he wore an abalone shell. The boys saw this and shot their arrows through it and killed him. When he died he fell to pieces; the pieces were rocks and scattered over the ground. Inside he was flesh like other people, but outside he was rock, except the place on his throat where the abalone shell was.

---

[31] The name *Loo'-poo-oi'-yes* means literally *the old man of rock*, from *loo'poo* rock, and *oi'yes* old man.

235

KA'-LUM-ME THE ROCK GIANT OF WENNOK VALLEY

The Olayome of Putah Creek say:

In a cave under the cliff on the east face of *Oo'-tel-tal-lah pow'-we*, a small mountain southwest of the south end of Wennok Lake in Lake County, dwells *Kā'-lum-me* the Rock Giant. He used to roam about nights, catching Indians and carrying them off to his cave to eat. He has not done this for some time.

Scientific Names of the Animals

FOR purposes of exact identification the scientific names of the mammals, birds, reptiles and a few other animals mentioned in the text are here given. Most of these were originally First People; they turned into animals at or about the time real people were created.

The Indian names of the First People who turned into these animals are given at the beginning of each story.

MAMMALS

Antelope, *Antilocapra americana*
Badger, *Taxidea taxus neglecta*
Bear – See Black, Grizzly, and Cinnamon Bear
Black Bear, *Ursus americanus* (black phase)
Bobcat or Wildcat, *Lynx fasciatus pallescens*
Cinnamon Bear, *Ursus americanus* (brown or red phase)
Cougar, *Felis hippolestes*
Coyote, *Canis ochropus*
Deer, Columbia Blacktail, *Odocoileus columbianus*
Elk, *Cervus nannodes* (California Valley Elk)
Fox, See Gray Fox
Gopher, *Thomomys* – several species
Gray Tree Squirrel, *Sciurus fossor*

237

Grizzly Bear, *Ursus horribilis californicus*
Gray Fox, *Urocyon californicus*
Kangaroo Rat, *Perodipus streatori* (of the Sierra
foothills)
Mountain Lion – See Cougar
Raccoon, *Procyon psora*
Skunk (large kind), *Mephitis occidentalis*
Shrew, *Sorex vagrans*
Timber-wolf, *Canis*
Weasel, *Putorius xanthogenys*
White-footed Mouse, *Peromyscus gambeli*
Woodrat, *Neotoma fuscipes streatori* (of the
Sierra foothills)

BIRDS

Barn Owl, *Aluco pratincola*
Blackbird, Redwing, *Agelaius* (considered the
male) and Brewer Blackbird, *Euphagus* (con-
sidered the female)
Bluejay, California, *Aphelocoma californica*
Bluejay, Mountain or Crested, *Cyanocitta stel-
leri frontalis*
Condor, *Gymnogyps californianus*
Crow, *Corvus brachyrhynchos hesperis*
Dove, *Zenaidura macroura carolinensis*
Eagle, Bald or White-headed, *Haliæetus leuco-
cephalus*
Eagle, Golden, *Aquila chrysaetos*
Falcon, Peregrine or Duck-hawk, *Falco pere-
grinus anatum*

Falcon, Prairie, *Falco mexicanus*

Goose, Canada or Black-necked, *Branta canadensis*

Goose, Gray, *Anser albifrons gambeli*

Grebe (small) or Helldiver, *Podilymbus podiceps*

Heron, Great Blue, *Ardea herodias*

Humming-bird – several species

Mallard Duck, *Anas platyrhynchos*

Meadowlark, *Sturnella neglecta*

Nuthatch, *Sitta carolinensis aculeata*

Owl, Great Horned, *Bubo virginianus pacificus*

Quail, California, *Lophortyx californicus*

Raven, *Corvus corax sinuatus*

Red-shafted Flicker, *Colaptes cafer collaris*

Robin, *Planesticus migratorius propinquus*

Sandhill Crane, *Grus mexicana*

Sapsucker, *Sphyrapicus ruber*

Screech Owl, *Otus asio bendirei*

Spoonbill or Shoveler Duck, *Spatula clypeata*

Turkey Buzzard, *Cathartes aura septentrionalis*

Wren, Tule, *Telmatodytes palustris paludicola*

REPTILES

Frog, *Rana draytoni*

Lizard, Black, *Sceloporus biseriatus* (black phase)

Lizard, Blue-sided, *Sceloporus occidentalis*

Lizard, Fire, *Crotophytus silus*

Lizard, Little, *Sceloporus graciosus*

Rattlesnake, *Crotalus lucifer*
Toad, *Bufo halophilus*
Turtle, *Clemmys marmorata*

INSECTS AND OTHER INVERTEBRATES

Common Fly – several species
Poison Spider, *Lathrodectus mactens*
Yellowjacket Wasp, *Vespa* (several species)
Money Clam (thick northern species), *Saxidomus giganteus*
Money Clam (common species), *Saxidomus nuttalli*
Abalone, *Haliotis* (several species)

Scientific Names of the Trees and other Plants

Buckeye, *Aesculus californica*
Buttonball bush, *Cephalanthus occidentalis*
Cane or Reed, *Phragmites vulgaris*
Cedar, Incense, *Libocedrus decurrens*
Elderberry, *Sambucus glauca*
Madrone, *Arbutus menziesi*
Manzanita, *Arctostaphylos* (several species)
Oak, Black, *Quercus californica*
Oak, Blue, *Quercus douglasi*
Oak, Valley or Water, *Quercus lobata*
Pine, Digger, *Pinus sabiniana*
Pine, Sugar, *Pinus lambertiana*
Pine, Yellow, *Pinus ponderosa*
Sage-herb, *Artemisia ludoviciana*
Sycamore, *Platinus racemosa*

𝔅ibliography of California Mythology[32]

Barrett, S. A. "A Composite Myth of the Pomo Indians," in the *Journal of American Folk-lore* (Boston, 1906), vol. xix, 37-51.

Boscana. "Chinigchinich" [Luiseño] in A. Robinson's *Life in California* (New York, 1846).

Burns, L. M. "'Digger' Indian Legends" [Scott Valley Shasta], in *Land of Sunshine* (Los Angeles, 1901), vol. xiv, 130-134; 223-226; 310-314; 397-402.

Chambers, G. A. [Fragment of a Mermaid story from the Chico Midoo], in the *Journal of American Folk-lore* (1906), vol. xix, 141.

Clark, Galen. *Indians of Yosemite Valley* [Southern Me-wuk], (Yosemite Valley, Calif., 1904), chap. vii, "Myths and Legends."

Curtin, Jeremiah. *Creation Myths of Primitive America* [Wintoon and Yana tribes], (Boston, 1898).

—— Achomawi Myths, edited by Roland Dixon, in *Journal of American Folk-lore* (1909), vol. xxii, 283-287.

Denny, Melcena Burns. "Orleans Indian Legends" [Karok or Kworatem], in *Out West* (Los Angeles, Calif.), vol. xxv (1906), 37-40; 161-166; 268-271; 373-375; 451-454; vol. xxvi (1907), 73-80; 168-170; 267-268.

Dixon, Roland B. "Some Coyote Stories from the Maidu

---

[32] Ethnologists and others should take greater care in the identification of the personages mentioned in the myths. The value of many of the papers whose titles are here given is materially lessened by false identifications of the animal people.

243

Indians of California," in the *Journal of American Folk-lore* (1900), vol. xiii, 267-270.

DIXON, ROLAND B. "Maidu Myths," in the American Museum of Natural History *Bulletin* (New York, 1902), vol. xvii, part ii, 33-118.

—— "System and Sequence in Maidu Mythology," in the *Journal of American Folk-lore* (1903), vol. xvi, 32-36.

—— "Mythology of the Shasta-Achomawi," in the *American Anthropologist* (Washington, D.C., 1905), vol. vii, 607-612.

—— "Achomawi and Atsugewi Tales," in the *Journal of American Folk-lore* (1908), vol. xxi, 159-177.

DuBOIS, CONSTANCE GODDARD. "Mythology of the Diegueños," in the *Journal of American Folk-lore* (1901), vol. xiv, 181-185.

—— "The Story of Chaup: A Myth of the Diegueños," in the *Journal of American Folk-lore* (1904), vol. xvii, 217-242.

—— "Mythology of the [Luiseño] Mission Indians," in the *Journal of American Folk-lore*, vol. xvii (1904), 185-188; vol. xix (1906), 52-60; 145-164.

—— "The Raven of Capistrano" [Luiseño], in *Out West* (1907), vol. xxvi, 430-437; 537-544; vol. xxvii, 57-64; 152-157; 227-233; 343-351; 415-421; 523-531.

—— "Religion of the Luiseño Indians of Southern California. Myths," in the California University publications on *American Archæology and Ethnology* (Berkeley, Calif., 1908), vol. viii, 128-157.

—— "The Spirit Wife – A Mission Myth (elaborated)," in the *Southern Workman* (Hampton, Va., 1908), vol. xxxvii, 477-480; 512.

—— "Ceremonies and Traditions of the Diegueño Indians" [with fragment of a Yuma creation myth], in the *Journal of American Folk-lore* (1908), vol. xxi, 228-236.

GODDARD, PLINY EARLE. "Hupa Texts," in the California University publications on *American Archæology and Ethnology* (1904), vol. i.

GODDARD, PLINY EARLE. "Lassik Tales," in the *Journal of American Folk-lore* (1906), vol. xix, 133-140.

——"Kato Texts. Translations," in the California University publications on *American Archæology and Ethnology* (1909), vol. v, 183-238.

HARRINGTON, JOHN PEABODY. "A Yuma Account of Origins," in the *Journal of American Folk-lore* (1908), vol. xxi, 324-338.

HUDSON, J. W. "An Indian [Yokut] Myth of the San Joaquin Basin," in the *Journal of American Folk-lore* (1902), vol. xv, 104-106.

JOHNSTON, ADAM. [Fragment of a "Po-to-yan-te" Yokut Creation Myth] in H. R. Schoolcraft's *Indian Tribes* (Washington, D.C., 1854), vol. iv, 224-225.

KROEBER, A. L. "Wishosk Myths," in the *Journal of American Folk-lore* (1905), vol. xviii, 85-107.

—— "Indian Myths of South Central California," [33] in the California University publications on *American Archæology and Ethnology* (1907), vol. iv, 169-250.

—— "Origin Tradition of the Chemehuevi Indians," in the *Journal of American Folk-lore* (1908), vol. xxi, 240-242.

—— "Two Myths of the [Luiseño] Mission Indians of California," in the *Journal of American Folk-lore* (1906), vol. xix, 309-321.

—— Notes on California Folk-lore. [A Luiseño Tale; Wiyot Folk-lore], in the *Journal of American Folk-lore* (1908), vol. xxi, 35-39.

KROEBER, HENRIETTE ROTHSCHILD. "Wappo Myths" [The Two Brothers; The Coyote and the Frog], in the *Journal of American Folk-lore* (1908), vol. xxi, 321-323.

—— "California Indian Legends" [The Pleaides, a "Southern

---

[33] Mainly Yokut, but comprising also six important fragments of "Rumsien Costanoan" [Kah'-koon A-chēs-ta], four second-hand fragments of "Pohonichi Miwok" [Southern Mewuk], and one "Gitanemuk Shoshonian" [Ke'-tah-na-mwa-kam or Tejon Serrano].

California" Myth; The Theft of Fire, a Yokut Myth], in *Out West* (1908), vol. xxviii, 66-69.

POWERS, STEPHEN. *Tribes of California* (Contributions to North American Ethnology, Washington, D.C., 1877), vol. iii.

Contains myths of several tribes, very loosely rendered.

RIED, HUGO. [Fragments of Gabrielino or Tong-vā Myths, collected in 1852], in the Essex Institute *Bulletin* (Salem, Mass., 1885), vol. xvii, 15-17; 18-26.

SPARKMAN, P. S. "A Luiseño Tale," in the *Journal of American Folk-lore* (1908), vol. xxi, 35-36.

SPENCER, D. L. "Notes on the Maidu Indians of Butte County, California" [The Buumo Myth – Battle of the Coyote and Bat], in the *Journal of American Folk-lore* (1908), vol. xxi, 244-245.

STEWART, GEO. W. "Two Yokuts Traditions" [Fragments of Tache tales on the Origin of Fire, and the Turtle], in the *Journal of American Folk-lore* (1908), vol. xxi, 237-239.

—— "A Yokuts [Wiktchumne] Creation Myth," in the *Journal of American Folk-lore* (1906), vol. xix, 322.

WATERMAN, THOMAS. Analysis of the Mission Indian Creation Story, in the *American Anthropologist* (1909), vol. xi, 41-55.

NOTE. The author's manuscript of the bibliography has been altered somewhat in form to agree with the form preferred by the publisher.

Index

Index

ABALONE SHELL: conceals vulnerable spot on throat of Rock Giant 235; covers He'-koo-lās the Sun-woman 18, 201; scientific name 240. *See also* Ah'-wook.

Acorn mush or soup: 35, 38, 118, 173, 192.

Acorns: women pounding 35, 181; mother bear pounding 103, 106; pounded with stone pestles 125; planted by Bluejays 213.

Aesculus californica, Buckeye: 241. *See also* Oo'-noo.

Agelaius, Red-winged Blackbird: 238.

Ah-hā'-le (Southern Mewuk for Coyote-man): 27, 162, 165-167; how he stole the Sun 34-43; how he stole the Morning 44-46. *See also* Coyote-man.

Ah'-ut (Southern Mewuk for Crow): 162, 191-193. *See also* Crow.

Ah-wahn'-dah, guardian of the fire and sun (Southern Mewuk for Turtle): keeper of the Sun and fire 34, 39-40; keeper of the morning 44-46; sleeps with one eye open 39; falls asleep and loses the sun 40.

Ah-wah'-ne (Southern Mewuk for Yosemite Valley): 93, 229. *See also* Yosemite Valley.

Ah-wet'-che (Hoolpoomne for Crow): 66, 83, 84. *See also* Crow.

Ah'-wook, abalone shell: 18, 201, 240.

Al'-leh, the hand-game: 75-80.

Alphabet used for Indian words: 29.

Aluco pratincola, Barn Owl: 238.

American River: 54, 55, 230.

Amulet: 211. *See also* Wep'-pah.

Anas platyrhynchos, Mallard Duck: 239. *See also* Yow'-hah.

Ang-e'-sa-wä'-pah, place on Merced River: 169.

Animals: origin 17, 171-172: beliefs about 209-215.

Anser albifrons gambeli, Gray Goose: 239.

Antelope: 48, 49, 237.

Antilocapra americana: 237.

Aphelocoma californica, California Valley Bluejay: 238. *See also* Ti'-e-te.

Aquila chrysaetos, Golden Eagle: 238. *See also* We-pe-ah'-gah and We'-wis-sool.

Arbutus menziesi, Madrone tree: 241.

Arctostaphylos, Manzanita: 241.

Ardea herodias, Great Blue Heron: 239.

Artemisia ludoviciana, Sage-herb: 136, 159, 241.

Aw'-kim, place in upper foothills between Middle and South

249

251

255

159, 167; people made from 159;
scientific name 241.

Map showing distribution of Mewan tribes: 25.

Mariposa Mewuk: 34, 35, 92, 116,
211, 213, 218.

Mā'-wā (Northern Mewuk for
Gray Squirrel): 222.

Meadowlark: hunted by Wek'-wek
138, 139; understands Indian
languages 113; says disagreeable things 213, 219; if egg
broken, rain falls 212-213;
ghosts of bad Indians turn into
219; scientific name 239. *See
also* Hoo-yu'-mah and Yu-koo'-
le.

Meadowlark-man: 54-56, 58, 59;
prevented immortality 19, 55-
56, 132, 212; prevented Lizard-
man from turning into the Moon
59; prevented Lizard from
bringing dead back to life 55;
prevented Wek'-wek from bringing dead wife to life 131-132.
See also Hool, Yu'-ka-loo, and
Yu-koo'-le.

Me'-cham yem'-me-um, ashes and
burnt bones of dead: 227.

Mel'-le-a-loo'-mah hills (Tuleyome): 139.

Mel'-ling-i'-yah (Northern Mewuk for Yellowjacket Wasp):
222.

Mephitis occidentalis, Skunk: 238.
See also His'-sik.

Merced Falls: 169.

Merced River: 162, 169, 229.

Mermaids or Water-women: 20,
66, 81, 228-230. *See also* Ho-
hā'-pe, Ho-sā'-pah, and Hoo-
soo'-pe.

Mewan Mythology: fundamental
elements 18-20; minor beliefs
20-21; local or tribal myths 21-
22; ancient myths 31-205; present day myths 207.

Mewan tribes: distribution 24;
map 25; language 24.

Mew'-ko, Indian people (in language of the Valley tribes):
how made 73, 83-87.

Me'-wuk, Chowchilla: 34, 44, 45,
217, 232.

Me'-wuk, Indian People: how
made 55, 101, 115. *See also*
People.

Me'-wuk tribes: territory 24, 31;
map 25.

Me'-wuk, Mariposa: 34, 35, 92,
211, 213, 218.

Me'-wuk, Merced River: 229.

Me'-wuk, Middle: eastern boundary 94; creation story 60-64;
story of Bear and Fawns 110-
112; beliefs about animals 210,
212, 213; beliefs about ghosts
218; origin of noise 224.

Me'-wuk, Northern: consider Coyote-man selfish 18; awe of feathers 20. *Myths*: how Robin got
his red breast 32-33; how Tol'-
le-loo got the fire 48-53; why
Lizard-man did not restore
the dead to life 54-56; Coyote-
man and Lizard-man 58-59;
how Ravens became people 101;
the Bear and the Fawns 102-
109; beliefs about Bears 209;
how the children of He-le'-jah
became people 115; Nek'-na-kā'-
tah the Rock-maiden 123; beliefs
about animals 209-210, 214; beliefs about ghosts 219, 220; the

260

fire for Mountain People 48-53; scientific name 238. *See also* Loo'-loo-e and White-footed Mouse.

To-lo'-mah (Southern Mewuk for Bobcat): 92, 93.

Tomales Bay, Marin County (home of Tam-mal'-ko, part of Hoo'-koo-e'-ko tribe): 18, 20, 66, 198, 200; home of survivors 24; story told at 204; belief as to Ducks and Geese 214; source of big money clam 215; belief as to Ghosts 217; belief as to Rainbow 225; as to Echo 224; as to Witches 227; as to Pigmies and Water People 228.

Too'-cha-mo, the stump: 210. *See also* Stump.

Too-koo'-le (Northern Mewuk for Great Horned Owl): 219. *See also* Owl, Great Horned.

Too'-koom, the tree buckskin (a fungus): 149-150, 151.

Too'-le, a chief of the First People who became the Evening Star: 92-99; why he failed to kill Deer 98.

Too-le'-ze (Northern Mewuk for Timber-wolf): how he hunts deer 210.

Too'-pe, Kangaroo Rat: 23, 162, 163, 238.

Too'-wik (Southern Mewuk for the Badger): 21, 23, 116, 119, 237. *See also* Badger-woman.

Totem or guardian spirit: 222.

To-to'-ka-no (Southern Mewuk for Sandhill Crane): loud voice 23; chief of Valley People 34-43; refused to accept the Sun 42; scientific name 239. *See also* Sandhill Crane.

To-to'-kol (Wipa for Sandhill Crane): mother of Lo-wut 126-128. *See also* Sandhill Crane.

To-to'-kon (Southern Mewuk for Sandhill Crane): 162, 195-196, 239. *See also* Sandhill Crane.

Transformation: of First People into animals or objects 17, 18, 43, 87, 132, 171; of feathers, sticks, or clay into people 19-20, 86-87, 148-149, 167, 204-205.

Transmigration: 219.

Tule: 140, 144, 183. *See also* Kol.

Tule-wren: shot out the sun 21, 152-154; scientific name 239. *See also* Chā'-kā.

Tu'-le-yo'-me poo-koot, ancient home of tribe: 138, 139.

Tu'-le-yo'-me tribe: 20, 21, 24; how Sah'-te set the world on fire 138-151. *See also* O'-lā'-yo'-me.

Tuolumne Mewuk: 110, 210, 212, 218, 224.

Tuolumne River: 38, 60, 110, 210, 212, 218.

Tu'-pe (Southern Mewuk for Kangaroo Rat-woman): 23, 162, 163, 238. *See also* Kangaroo Rat.

Turkey Buzzard: 48, 49, 84; a wicked chief 162, 184-187; wing bone used in witchcraft 227-228; scientific name 239. *See also* Choo'-hoo, Ho'-ho and Hoo'-a-zoo.

Turtle: keeper of the sun or fire 34, 39, 42; keeper of the morning 44-46; sleeps with one eye open 39; falls asleep and loses